AGRICULTURE UNDER COMMUNISM

Agriculture
Under Communism

A BACKGROUND BOOK

Lord Walston

DUFOUR EDITIONS

CHESTER SPRINGS

PENNSYLVANIA

Contents

1

Introduction

DESPITE the rapid advance of industrialisation during the past 100 years, agriculture still remains the most important occupation of mankind. In some parts of the world the richest people are found among bankers, manufacturers, traders, or oil magnates: but it is salutary to remember that while the producer of food can, and often does, survive without in any way being dependent upon such people, even the greatest tycoon in his air-conditioned office, insulated by his millions from the ordinary world, cannot survive for twenty-four hours without the help of the farmer or the peasant. His breakfast of bacon and eggs, bread, coffee and sugar; his midday steak, his whisky and his wine, would never have appeared on his table had not some worker on the land, somewhere in the world, sweated to produce them; and even in this age of artificial fibres, his coat and his trousers, his shoes and very possibly his socks and his shirt, are in the main the produce of the land.

Yet how much thought does this great man give to those who provide him with those things without which, for all his bank balances in the financial centres of the world, he would be unable to survive? And how much thought do more ordinary mortals, as they travel daily to their factories or offices, give to these same producers of food, drink and clothing? And which among the hundreds of millions of workers on the land throughout the world have any conception of the importance, the absolute need, of their work to the survival of every living person?

Civilisation has developed in such a way that power over others now appears to reside in the hands, not of those who produce the essential of life—food: not even of those who wield the greatest military power: but of those who control the money. But in fact money is only of indirect importance: it gives power only if it enables its possessors to control what is needed for life and for survival: and among these essentials are weapons of defence—and offence; fuel, and above all, food. Even in Europe, until comparatively recent times, this was apparent; in India, China, the Soviet Union, and the continents of Africa and South America, it is still apparent today. In these vast areas the ownership or the control of land confers political power. It is for this reason that the agrarian picture—not the techniques of soil cultivation or animal husbandry, but the ownership of the land, the division of the reward between owner and actual cultivator, whether the owner be a private individual, a corporation, or the State, the power of the owner over the surrounding community—is of overriding importance in the political scene.

There are many countries in the world today which bear this out. In Egypt, for instance, and in the Middle East, as well as in Southern Italy, are seen the political implications of the agrarian question—the reaction of the cultivator against the owner, against what is to his mind the undue share of the crop taken by someone who has done nothing to produce it other than to own the land upon which it is grown; and against the lack of opportunity which effectively makes it impossible for him ever to acquire land of his own.

It is also seen in East Africa where primitive systems of tribal ownership exist side by side with modern capitalistic agriculture, and where the beginnings of urban industrialisation show the opportunities that are available, albeit still only for a few. It is the most pressing problem facing Communist governments not only in the Soviet Union but also in China, Poland, Hungary and Yugoslavia. Here the governments may have to reconcile their political theories with the need of their people for food, and attempt to come to terms with the innate resistance of the cultivator of the soil to inter- ference from government, of no matter what complexion.

This book describes briefly some of the methods by which Communist governments in different countries have attempted to solve this problem. It also tries to assess the success or failure of these attempts. But a bare recital of governmental action and cultivators' reaction since the replacement of former régimes by Communism is of little value. Such changes as have taken place, for example in Russia, in the last 45 years are of enormous contemporary importance: but their true significance can only be judged in the context of history. What is more, the probable results of similar changes in other countries can only be assessed with any hope of accuracy if the background to those changes which have already taken place is fully understood and compared with the past history of those countries where a new system is contemplated. To help the reader to form his own opinion on these matters some space must be devoted to history— not enough to entitle this work to be called a history book, but, it is hoped, enough to place in its proper perspective such evidence as can be gathered from the present century.

As one makes a short study of the agrarian history of different countries it is tempting to believe that there is a regular pattern of development. This pattern would begin with the nomadic tribe, wandering with its flocks over huge uninhabited tracts of land, resting in one place so long as water and fodder are plentiful, and game is there for the hunting, and moving on in search of fresh supplies when any of these are exhausted. The

next stage is one of settlement in a particularly favourable spot. Here land would be cleared, not by individuals
for their own use, but communally, by the whole tribe:
crops would be planted and reaped and stored, and
cattle would be moved comparatively short distances to
wherever the best pasture was to be found—just as today
in many Arab countries the Bedouins move their flocks
from plains to mountains, depending on the season,
plant crops in a suitable spot, and then move on, to return later to harvest them when they are ready.

As the comforts of a settled life come to be felt and
appreciated, so does even seasonal movement disappear.
Members of the tribe build themselves permanent dwellings, and come to look upon plots of land as their own
private possession, and the crops grown on them destined
for their own private use, rather than for the enjoyment
of the whole tribe. At this stage there is still ample land
for all: anyone who is prepared to clear the scrub or
forest is welcome to do so. But as this settled life
develops so does specialisation. No longer do people
regard themselves primarily as members of the tribe,
fighting, hunting and cultivating side by side for the
common good. Their loyalty becomes increasingly confined to their own family, and the crafts that they
practise are increasingly for the benefit of this family.
One family may be carpenters, one blacksmiths, one
harness-makers. These have no time to produce all of
their own food, and what they do not produce they obtain by exchanging with others the results of their craft
for food.

So, very slowly over the centuries, grows up a society
where food is produced not just for consumption by the
tribe or even by the family, but for exchange. And it
follows that he who can grow the greatest amount of
food will have the greatest amount of surplus which he
can exchange for other things. So arises competition for

land, and also for labour with which to cultivate the land. In this competition the most successful is either the military leader, as in Europe during the feudal period; or, in more settled and peaceful times, the cultivator who has amassed enough surplus to become a moneylender, or banker: or the merchant who sells on credit to the poor cultivator, taking his land as security. And there are many countries in the world today where this process still continues.

This, then, is the period of production for private profit, as it is found in most parts of the world today. But in Communist theory, and to a large extent, as will be seen, in actual practice in those countries where there are Communist governments, this type of production has been replaced by production for the State. The State owns the land and plans the production. The workers are State servants, receiving wages and perhaps a share of the profit, but no longer individual farmers, free to rise by their own skill and initiative, or fall by the lack of it.

But this general pattern is an over-simplification. If a community could be found that was completely isolated from the outside world, it might well develop in such a manner. But today there are, even more than in the past, innumerable outside influences which come to bear on development. Even without deliberate interference by another country anxious to see its own particular way of life spreading throughout the world, radio and cinema, books and newspapers, and above all travel, open the eyes of those in developing countries to what is going on elsewhere. Men leave their own country and visit others: there they see new methods which appeal to them and which, on their return home, they try to get accepted by their own people.

But frequently these new methods that look so good in another country have only been achieved after centuries of slow evolution, or after decades of painful revolution. Many of them can only succeed where there is already in existence a highly developed system of communications which enables the specialised product of one area to pass safely and cheaply to another distant part of the country where it is needed: or where there is a legal system defining the rights and obligations of landowner and cultivator, of farmer and farmworker, of buyer and seller, of merchant, producer and consumer. Others can succeed only where there is ample skilled labour available, and skilled labour can only come from good education at all levels—in the villages, for the children of the countryside, in the market towns for the higher levels of local instructors and managers of large units, and in the universities of the great cities for the professors and research workers.

Where it is attempted to introduce systems from other countries which depend upon some or all of these conditions, and where these conditions do not exist in the country which is adopting the new systems, difficulties, often serious, are bound to arise. On the other hand, if change is stubbornly resisted, and the lessons that can be learned from other countries ignored, not only is the standard of life kept unnecessarily low, but the change, when it comes, will come with the violence of the French or Russian revolution, rather than with the peaceful transition that has characterised the movement of British agriculture from the pre-Norman Conquest type of tribal cultivation, through feudal, to the commercial agriculture of today, this commercial agriculture itself having passed through the period of unfettered private enterprise in the eighteenth and nineteenth centuries to the present time when leases between landowner and tenant, rates and hours of pay for farmworkers, prices, and in some cases quantities, of crops, are all regulated by the State.

Such changes have been taking place with varying degrees of rapidity throughout the whole world over many centuries. The chapters that follow will describe in greater detail some of the results of these changes in countries where attempts have been made to put the Communist theory into practice. But these changes must not be looked on as academic exercises, worked out in the remote studies of professors, or in the offices of politicians or bureaucrats. They are changes which affect intimately the lives of everyone. If they succeed, in the technical sense, they will result in greater food production in the world. This in itself is of prime importance, for even today, at the present figure of world population, hundreds of millions of people are suffering from not having enough food to eat. As world population increases this shortage will become even more marked unless food production increases even more rapidly than does population. But if these changes result in a decline in production, or in a rate of expansion slower than would have taken place had other methods been adopted, then not only the country in which the experiment has been made will suffer, but the whole world will be the poorer.

Even this aspect of the agrarian problem is perhaps a little remote. Apart from the famines which have resulted, and may still result, following upon an enforced change in systems of farming and land ownership—and both the Soviet Union and China have given examples of this in the not far distant past—any changes in total quantities of food produced are usually slow to make themselves felt and are spread over so many people that the effect on the individual consumer is relatively slight. But the individual producer is affected in an entirely different way. A change of system for him means an entirely new form of life, new methods of working, new hopes and ambitions, new fears and uncertainties.

For some the change may mean release from bondage and poverty; for others it may mean the abandonment of all those things which bring joy to life. For the majority it will undoubtedly bring some happiness and some sadness. But whatever the effects it must above all be remembered by the innovators that they are not planning with pawns on a chess-board, or with figures in a ledger, but with men and women, with ordinary people performing ordinary tasks—and what is more, with a class of people who in fact make up the great majority of the world's population, those who cultivate the soil.

Even if a new system resulted in greater efficiency, even if more food were eventually produced, the hopes and happiness of these people, these human beings, must not be pushed ruthlessly to one side. Change and improvement must come, but it is the duty of the innovator to see that with this change, and with these improvements the cultivators themselves lead a better and a happier life.

2

The Russian Background

Russia in the fifteenth century bore little resemblance to the great empire of the later Czars or to the Russia of today. Then, and for several centuries after, it covered a comparatively restricted area in Eastern Europe and consisted of a series of loosely knit and sometimes independent duchies, principalities and city states, owing a form of feudal allegiance to a variety of overlords but each, for the most part, pursuing its own way, and relying for its needs upon its own resources. The great source of riches came partly from the export of timber from the forests of the north, but especially from the export of furs from the animals found in those parts; but most regions were self-sufficient in food. Land was plentiful and was in the first instance cultivated in a tribal manner, though in many regions, especially in the South, nomadic and semi-nomadic pastoral life persisted for a long time, the need for more land being met simply by cutting down or burning forests.

By degrees the European feudal pattern established itself, large tracts of land being given by a conquering leader to his followers as a means of ensuring the loyalty of the newly acquired territory. In 1478 Ivan the Great brought to an end the long rivalry between Moscow and Novgorod by the subjugation of the latter, but in the territories that he obtained in this way he did not set up feudal estates. Instead, he ensured the cultivation of the land by placing on it peasants who were in fact State serfs, but who were free from many of the irksome detailed duties to which the serfs of private lords were subject: meanwhile the merchants of Novgorod continued to add to their wealth and develop their commerce without taking any interest in land ownership or in food production.

In fact the land itself was valueless in its natural state: to produce wealth it was essential to have labour, and it was the ownership of this labour, in the form of serfs, that gave both wealth and power. Then, and for many centuries after, a landowner's wealth was measured not in terms of the ownership of so many acres, but of so many 'souls' or, more accurately, 'bodies' on whom he could call for work. Even today in parts of the Middle East one still hears talk of a rich man owning a certain number of villages, meaning the people living in them, rather than a certain number of acres.

This was the picture when Peter the Great came to the throne in 1703. The nobles and the clergy alone were entitled to own slaves or serfs, and the main agricultural area was the Moscow Plain. In the more distant parts methods of cultivation had progressed hardly at all from the Middle Ages, shifting population still persisted in many areas, forests being cleared by burning and cultivated for forty or fifty years until their goodness was exhausted, when the tribes moved on to fresh areas which were similarly treated, leaving previously cultivated areas to regenerate naturally. In some districts where the serfs had land that they could cultivate for their own use these lands were subject to periodic redistribution by the lord, thus discouraging anything but the most exhausting forms of agriculture. To the North were the forests, still producing fur and timber, these still the greatest sources of Russia's wealth, while to the South along the Don the Cossacks, reinforced by runaway slaves and army deserters, were acting as unofficial colonisers of the intrinsically fertile Steppe land.

In the Moscow Plain itself, and in some other advanced

areas, cultivation was closer to that which was found at the same period in Western Europe. The three-field system had been introduced some 100 years earlier, villages were appearing at the centre of the three fields, and each family of serfs had its own strip, held at the lord's pleasure, in each field.

Under Peter great strides were made in the industrialisation of the country. Iron foundries and textile mills were established and merchants were forced to use some of their profits from trading to supply capital for these new industrial ventures. Labour was provided by transferring serfs from State lands to the new foundries and factories,* and at the same time communications were improved mainly by making use of existing waterways and by building canals.

This laid the foundation for a departure from subsistence agriculture to one based on sale. Further impetus was given to increased agricultural output by freeing all slaves, or rather by changing their status from that of slave to that of serf. This was no liberal measure, but was done solely as a means of raising revenue. The freed slaves were now liable to poll tax but they were still bound as tight as ever to their master. It was he who determined the number of days' service they had to perform (sometimes up to six days a week) and the levy they must pay; it was he who allocated their land, controlled their marriages, and could still treat them as his chattels, even to the extent of buying and selling them. Nor were they allowed to leave the estate without a passport granted by the lord.

These changes brought about by Peter, coupled with

* Contemporary Russia profits from this precedent. Recently one of the Soviet Ministers responsible for the reclamation of vast tracts of Siberia told me that, although faced with many difficulties, lack of labour was not one of them. 'If we do not get enough volunteers we simply transfer labour from those areas where we have a surplus.'

17

his reform of the nobility and changes in the laws of inheritance, increased the tendency of landowners to live either at Court or in provincial capitals away from their estates. This in turn encouraged them to spend more money than would have been the case had they remained on their estates, and thus brought about an increased pressure on peasants and serfs to provide larger revenues for the landowners.

It would have been possible to produce this increased wealth without hardship had there been an educated and interested leadership from the landowners to introduce from Western countries improved farming techniques. But this leadership was not forthcoming: the result for peasants and serfs alike was increased hardship, revolt and flight. There had already been important revolts of serfs, such as those of Bolotnikov in 1606, of Stenka Razin in 1670, of Bulavin in 1707; but the revolt led by Pugachov in 1773 was the most serious. Pugachov promised the abolition of serfdom and the granting of land to the former serfs. In words similar to those of modern leaders he called upon the serfs and peasants to rally to him. 'We grant to all hitherto in serfdom and subjugation to the landowners . . . liberty and freedom . . . with possession of the land, the woods, the hay meadows, the fishing grounds, the salt lakes, without payment and without rent and we free all those hitherto oppressed by the malefactor landowner and the bribe-taking officials and judges. . . .'

But after two years Pugachov's revolt was suppressed and conditions in the countryside remained unaltered. Meanwhile the landowner's need for more money grew. He refused to abandon his ambitions at Court and to return to the simple life in the country: so the frequent result for the landowner was debt, mortgage, foreclosure and even bankruptcy, with the land passing increasingly into the hands of the rich merchants. For the serf it meant increased pressure, increased exertion, and an even greater poverty. But it also led to increased colonisation of the rich black-earth areas of the Steppes between the Volga and the Urals, and many large and wealthy estates were founded for this reason at that time.

In general, throughout the eighteenth century and the early part of the nineteenth century, this type of colonisation continued far into the South, lonely outposts being replaced by the local estates of noblemen from the North. A few small State peasants remained, but in general the life of the cultivator of the countryside was in the hands of the great landowners cultivating through serfs.

It was at this period that the village community or 'mir' took on an even greater importance than it had hitherto enjoyed. The 'mir' was the unofficial but recognised grouping together of the non-free members of the agricultural community or manor. As to its remote origins historians disagree. It is, however, clear that all early communities have a loose tribal organisation, to which strangers may be admitted if they come to settle in the village, but which consists solely of those whose life is bound together geographically and economically. Community discipline is maintained by the tribal elders, usually elected by the whole male community; these elders may also have some control over inter-marriage, and must ensure the survival of the group by regulating land use and grazing. The Russian 'mir' was organised in just this way and in particular the communal land was periodically redistributed by these village elders, in order to prevent any one family or individual getting sole benefit from the most fruitful areas.

As provincial and central government stretched out farther to affect the lives of the villages, even though the landowner had the legal responsibility, it was to one of the serfs, the appointed and accepted head of the community, that the owner or the government official looked

19

for the implementation of the law or the edict. This quasi-official was ultimately responsible not only, as in the past, for the fair and proper cultivation of the communal land, for village discipline and for purely internal village affairs: he became, as time went on, responsible for the collection of the poll tax, for the selection of men for military service, and in general matters acted as the intermediary between the villages, the landowner and the government official.

So, throughout the eighteenth century and for the first 60 years of the nineteenth century, Russia remained unchanged in its social structure. Not only did the Czar retain absolute and unquestioned authority, as he did for another half-century longer, but the country remained rigidly divided into social classes out of which it was almost impossible to move. The largest of these consisted of about 50 million people out of a total of 60 million in European Russia, who were the serfs, deprived of virtually all freedom and constrained to produce that wealth on which the minority of the population prospered; and also to provide the soldiers needed by the country's rulers to preserve order and to protect and at times enlarge its frontiers.

The reforms of Peter the Great had strengthened the monarchy against the landowners, and in consequence had been strongly resisted by the latter. But after his death they regained some of their power and by 1785 they were strong enough to persuade Catherine the Great to put into the hands of the local nobility the official administration of justice and the maintenance of order in their own provinces. At the same time, as in other European countries, the last traces of justification for the privileges of the nobility had disappeared. So long as the nobles had obligations for service towards the Crown they could claim that these justified the service they in turn exacted from those beneath them. But when in 1762

Peter III agreed to the release of the nobility from all obligation to serve, the pattern of feudal service was finally destroyed and all that remained were the material advantages to be gained by the owners of serfs from the serfs themselves.

So great was the outcry by the serfs against this injustice that Peter agreed to their liberation: but he was deposed and later murdered and his edict was never implemented. Nevertheless the evils and injustices of serfdom were recognised by many, and strong pressure for its abolition was started. Nicholas the First wrote: 'Serfdom is the indubitable evil of Russian life but I think it still more dangerous to touch it.'

In spite of the all-pervading power of the State and the landowner the countryside was far from peaceful. Throughout the first half of the 19th century many outbreaks of violence occurred. In the five years before the final emancipation of the serfs there were over 400 serious risings and prior to that many hundreds of serf-owners or their agents had been killed. Although a minority of Russian landowners were the polished aristocrats of the salons of St. Petersburg and Moscow, Paris and Vienna, and although a majority were coarse and uneducated country squires not unlike the English equivalent of the eighteenth century, the liberal-minded leaders of the campaign for the liberation of the serfs were themselves landowners, as were the great writers, the teachers and leaders of thought of the period—men like Turgenev, Tolstoy, Lermontov and Gogol. But their fight was a hard one: serfdom, a stratified society, and the existing system of landownership were all too strongly entrenched to be easily overthrown.

However, at last in 1861, after the military failure of the Crimean War, Alexander II felt himself strong enough, or rather felt that the nobility was weak enough, for him to emancipate the 50 million serfs of European

Russia. Over half of these were State serfs, or serfs tied to factories or other non-agricultural enterprises: but 20 million of them were the property of some 260,000 private landowners, some owning 10 to 12, but others, the vastly rich nobles, counting their serfs by the thousands or tens of thousands. Little wonder that such a huge operation required, before it could succeed, the pressure of a world movement (France abolished serfdom in 1789, the Austrian Empire and Prussia removed the final traces in 1849, and in the United States slavery came to an end in 1865) allied to the ever-increasing need for labour of rising industrialisation. Even then success would not have come so quickly had not the position of the old-established and static landed aristocracy been seriously weakened by defeats of the army, of which they, by supplying the officers, were the backbone, and by their failure to retain their economic pre-eminence in the face of the challenge from merchants, industrialists and bankers.

So, at last, serfdom was abolished and the serfs became, in the eyes of law, free men. But freedom is a word of many meanings. When the serfs were freed it is true that they were no longer possessed by an individual land-owner, they were no longer under legal obligation to work for another, they were no longer liable to be bought or sold. Yet the need to work remained, or how else could they survive? And freedom to move, although not restricted by being the chattels of others, was still restricted by government action. The land which the serf had formerly cultivated for his own use but which in law belonged to his master, was now in law his own, or belonging to the 'mir' of which he was a member; but for all that it had to be paid for by way of an annual charge to the Government in addition to the existing poll tax to which every liberated serf was subject.

Thus his life remained hard—in some cases perhaps

even harder than when he had been a serf. If he worked well he might earn money in excess of his immediate needs; but if he worked badly or for any reason incurred the dislike of his employer he might find himself without a job, and at the same time without food or shelter.

As for the land which formerly had been cultivated on a communal basis by the members of the 'mir', the entitlement to the use of this was in theory the recompense for the service owed by them as serfs to the landowner. When these services came to an end the State bought out the landlords (and in this way staved off for a few more years the bankruptcy with which many of them were faced) and the liberated serfs found themselves saddled with an additional financial burden in the shape of a redemption annuity payable to the State, out of which the former serf-owners received their recompense. So in effect a double burden was placed on the liberated serf. It was he, in the final analysis, who had to make good to the landowner the latter's loss both of land and of labour.

It was not long before differences in economic and social standing began to appear among the liberated serfs themselves. Some became landless labourers searching for jobs either in the countryside or in the factories. Others were peasants with plots of land too small for the support of their families, and therefore forced to supplement their incomes by outside work; still others became peasants capable of maintaining a passable standard of living from their own holdings: and on top of these there emerged a class of rich peasants, the kulaks, employing others and adding to their riches by dealing, by money-lending and by buying up the land both of the gentry who were in need of ready cash, and of the less successful peasants.

The result of this was that so far from reducing tension in the countryside the emancipation of the serfs was followed by growing rural disturbances throughout the next fifty years. At the beginning of the First World War it was estimated that two-thirds of the cultivable area of Russia was owned by peasants, but that over one-third of this land was owned by one-tenth of the peasants, the remaining nine-tenths sharing between them the other two-thirds. It was these nine-tenths who were living in conditions of poverty and even starvation probably as bad as anything their forefathers had faced under serfdom.

This poverty and unrest gave rise to the revolution of 1905, with its burning of country houses and destruction of crops. This was countered by the agrarian reforms of Stolypin, Nicholas II's prime minister. First he set about breaking the influence of the 'mir', secondly he accelerated the consolidation of holdings, took away from the 'mir' its power of periodical redistribution of land, made peasant holdings hereditary, and put new life into the Peasants' Land Bank.

These reforms had their effect: technical progress advanced comparatively rapidly, the standard of living of the successful peasant rose, and a rural middle class developed: but there still was suffering among millions of small peasants and labourers and rural unrest remained. With the countryside in such a state it was unable to withstand the pressures of the First World War and the Russian Revolution became inevitable. As in France 125 years earlier, the theoretical impetus did not come from the land, nor was it the country-dwellers who lit the fuse: but it was in the countryside mainly that the explosive lay: without that explosive the fuse would have been lit in vain.

3

Agrarian Policy

THE Russian Revolution of 1917 stemmed from a long history of dissatisfaction with the government and with social conditions under the Czars, but it drew its immediate inspiration from the specific ideology contained in the writings of Marx and Engels. Although Engels had experience in the world of business, which was lacking in Marx, and although Marx in particular had close contacts with the intellectual Russian revolutionaries of his day, neither of them had anything but the most remote and theoretical acquaintance with agriculture, the land, or the people who worked on it.

It is probably for this reason that they were unduly optimistic concerning the difficulties inherent in bringing about, on a voluntary basis, particularly in countries at the stage of agrarian development in which most of Europe found itself in the middle of the nineteenth century, an agrarian structure which combined efficient production with communist principles. They were thus able to write 'We are firmly on the side of the small peasant, we shall do all that we can to make his life supportable, to help him on the road towards association with his fellows, if that is what he decides: but where he is not yet ready to make this decision we shall make every effort to give him as much time to ponder upon it on his little plot of land';* and 'When we take power we must not even think of expropriating the small peasant (whether with or without compensation) as we shall be obliged to do in the case of the large landowners. Our

* Engels, *Die Bauernfrage.*

task as regards the small peasant consists, in the first place, in bringing together their ownership and their cultivation of the land, and this will be done not by compulsion, but by example and the help of society.'*

Even Stalin, with his far closer knowledge of the Russian countryside, felt that he could write: 'A peasantry which has been through the school of three revolutions, which has fought the Czar, and the bourgeoisie, hand in hand with the workers, which has received from the hands of the workers both the soil and peace ... this offers especially fertile ground for economic collaboration with the workers.'†

Fortified by such hopes the Revolutionary Government of 1917 distributed among the peasants, and among the returning soldiers, all of whom came from peasant stock and most of whom had been taken from the land into the army, the land which had been taken from the landowners. The criterion was that of non-exploitation, in the strict Marxist sense—the land only for him who tills it. The tiller of the soil himself should enjoy the fruits of his labour, and others, landowners or large farmers employing hired labour, should not grow rich on the sweat of others.

One of the first Acts passed by the new Revolutionary Government was that concerning the land, designed to put into effect this principle, and to prevent any individual from owning more land than he and his family could cultivate. In this way the support of the peasant for the Revolution—never in fact in doubt—was assured: but at the same time, although the large landowner disappeared, the habit of the small peasant's renting his land, perhaps unofficially, to a larger and more prosperous neighbour, and even working for a cash wage, continued.

* *Selected Works of Marx and Engels*, Moscow 1948, vol. II, pp. 414–415.
  † Stalin, *Sočinenja*, vol. VI, pp. 132–133.

In fact by 1917, immediately before the Revolution, nearly 90 per cent of the arable land of European Russia was farmed by peasants, but a large part of this was held on tenancies from large landowners and the State, as well as on tenancies from the 'mir'. According to Bouvier,* 'Russian statistics of before the war (First World War), although inadequate, make it possible all the same to classify the different categories of agricultural properties according to their importance. In European Russia, so far as cultivable land is concerned, this order of importance was—on the eve of the Revolution—as follows:

1. Great estates (including those of the State and of absentee owners).
2. Communally-owned land (almost all of which consisted of "mir" land subjected to periodical redistribution, or cultivated on a communal basis).
3. Peasant land (including land belonging legally to the "mir", but escaping, either in law or in fact, from redistribution).
4. Land coming half-way between 2 and 3 ("degraded" communal land).

Altogether the two last categories equalled the communally-owned land. The agrarian system of Central Asia was either feudal or tribal. In Siberia, State land predominated, peasant properties coming into second place.'

Thus the problem of what to do with the land was neither so complicated as it was at the time of the French Revolution, nor as it was to be in such countries as Poland or Hungary some 30 years later when the large estates cultivated by the owners themselves were split up. In fact little more than 10 per cent of the entire area

* *La Collectivisation de l'Agriculture,* p. 24, footnote 6, Armand Colin. 1958.

became available for redistribution, although a considerable area which had found its way into the hands of the kulaks was returned to the 'mir', which then became responsible for handing it out among its members, according to their needs and to their ability to cultivate it—in other words, according to the size of their families.

A study of events after the French Revolution might have suggested that this redistribution of land, although on a minor scale, would lead to a food shortage in the towns. Those who benefited were those with least land and therefore those with the lowest standard of living— which at that level means with least to eat. Those from whom land was taken were those who produced the surplus from which the towns were fed. Even if the country had returned immediately to peace after the Revolution food shortage in the towns would certainly have been severe. But as it was, not only was great damage done to crops and to buildings during the actual Revolution itself, but fighting continued for many years afterwards, so the peasants were unable to settle down to uninterrupted cultivation.

The culmination came with the famine of 1921 and 1922, followed by disease, which affected not only the towns but also the actual food-producing areas themselves. The attitude of the peasants at this time is graphically described by Pasternak:

'The peasants are in revolt, there are ceaseless risings. You'll say that they are fighting the Reds or Whites indiscriminately, whoever may be in power, that they are simply against any established authority because they don't know what they want. Allow me to differ. The peasant knows very well what he wants, better than you or I do, but he wants something quite different. When the revolution came and woke him up, he decided that this was the fulfilment of his dreams, his ancient dream of living anarchically on his own land by the work of his hands, in complete independence and without owing anything to anyone. Instead of that, he found he had only exchanged the old oppression of the Czarist state for the new, much harsher yoke of the revolutionary super-state. Can you wonder that the villages are restless and can't settle down! . . .'*

There were those among the government who felt that the only solution to the problem lay in a tough attitude to the peasant. So long as private ownership of the land persisted, they argued, the very roots of the Communist society were in danger. If the land were to belong to the people it must belong equally to the factory worker as to the peasant, and individual ownership made this impossible. Even had the method of ensuring compulsory collections of food from the peasants been adequate (and even in a society with a highly developed and efficient bureaucracy such collections present insuperable difficulties) still there could be no ideological justification for the private ownership of one of the basic means of production. But less drastic councils prevailed, and not even Trotsky attempted to spread collective farms by compulsion. Such as had been started, largely by starving people from the towns in 1918, were a failure, and by 1920 less than 1 per cent of peasant families remained in these collectives.

To counteract the industrial stagnation and the failure of the peasant in his new liberty to meet the needs of the towns for food there was introduced in 1921 the New Economic Policy (N.E.P.). So far as the countryside was concerned this gave every appearance of being a retreat from Communist doctrine. Not only was private possession of the land retained, but specific encouragement was given to the kulak to acquire more acres, to employ others, and to accumulate wealth by his own efforts at the expense of others.

* Boris Pasternak, *Dr. Zhivago*, p. 202. Collins & Harvill Press. London 1958.

29

But the retreat was only tactical. In spite of the fine words of Marx and Engels, and even of Lenin, it was by now clearly recognised that there was an essential conflict between the peasant and Communism, and that the latter could never wholly triumph so long as the former survived. For purely technical reasons the peasant, and in particular the larger peasant, who was both more efficient than his smaller neighbour as well as being easier to deal with when it came to collecting food for the towns, was necessary. But as soon as the State was strong enough he would go. In the meantime, both for political reasons, as a counterweight on the side of the small peasant against the kulak, and as a practical measure in the longer term fight against the individual peasant, whether large or small, the co-operative principle was actively encouraged in the countryside.

The 'artel', a co-operative group based on particular trades or crafts, had long been known in Russia, and had something in common with the 'mir'; but it had never in the past been applied to agriculture. Marx indeed had condemned co-operative associations on the grounds that they perpetuated capitalism, though in a somewhat different form, and the early revolutionary leaders had followed this principle. But the new co-operative societies of the N.E.P. were a form of economic Trojan Horse.

In the first instance there was no question of co-operative exploitation of the soil: each peasant, however small, was still unquestioningly free to do this as an individual. The co-operatives were there to provide for the small peasants those advantages of buying and of processing which otherwise would have been available only to the kulaks. They were in fact not so much genuine co operatives as the provision by the State of certain services for people who were not equipped to provide these for themselves. As such they probably served a useful pur pose: but as a training ground for the future organisers of Soviet agriculture, and as a means of inserting Communist officials into the everyday life of the countryside, they were invaluable. It was because of the presence of these officials that in 1928 the government felt strong enough to declare war on the kulaks, or more precisely, on the whole peasantry, though for the moment it was against the kulaks alone that the battle was joined.

Stalin's hopes may have been genuine that 'by gradually permeating agriculture with the principles of collectivism—at first for the sale of agricultural produce, and in due course for agricultural production' the socialism of the towns would find its counterpart, by natural means once the last traces of feudalism had been removed, in the countryside; but after five years of the N.E.P. it was clear that such hopes were meeting with no success. Not only was a rural bourgeoisie, in the shape of the kulak, arising, but agricultural production was failing to respond to soft treatment. True, up till 1926 agriculture had recovered well from its disastrous days, and had by then reached the level in arable production, though not in livestock, of 1914. But from then production levelled out, and no technical progress came to help it expand still further.

At the same time, inequality was increasing rapidly. A 1929 census showed that in that year half the principal means of production (livestock, machinery etc.) were to be found on only one-sixth of the farms—those belonging to the kulaks. The kulak was growing rich, but the towns were no better fed. So began the third stage in the Russian agrarian revolution.

The aim was the ultimate abolition of all private property in land, and the substitution in its place of not only State-owned land but agricultural holdings operated directly for the benefit of the State rather than for the benefit of the cultivators. State farms did not provide the answer. They had already been tried and in the main had proved a failure. Even with willing workers the organisation and management of a huge agricultural enterprise is a highly skilled job for which few are qualified: when the labour for such an enterprise can only be drawn from among hostile, dispossessed peasants the task becomes virtually impossible.

The collective farm, or 'kolkhoz', provided the answer, and the previous existence of the 'mir', as well as of the recently formed supply co-operatives, made the problem easier. Peasants were invited to join together in a collective farm, bringing their land with them, and, in the initial stages, with the freedom to withdraw if they wished, taking with them their land or (an important reservation) a similar area of land in another part of the village. The incentive to the peasant to do this lay in the assistance which he had received from the co-operative, and which henceforth would only be available to members of the collective (this assistance meant the provision of good quality seeds, fertilisers, machinery and technical advice) and in more favourable delivery quotas. At the same time open war was declared upon the kulak, though care was taken to point out that it was only against the rich peasant, the enemy and oppressor of the poor, that action was being taken.

The action taken was ruthless and eventually effective —dispossession, without the right to join a kolkhoz, imprisonment, deportation, and death. In Panferov's novel 'Brusski' the official attitude towards the kulak is described by one of the characters: 'We must beat the idea of property out of a man just as dust is beaten out of a mattress. Since the peasant is trying to bargain with us, let us knock this wish out of his head.'

By 1930 the kulak had ceased to exist, and all that remained were a few State farms, and collective farms nd small peasants employing none other than family labour. The rise in the number of collective farms was reat. In October 1929 only 4 per cent of the peasant amilies were members of a kolkhoz; by March 1930 the umber had risen to 58 per cent. But although recruits vere in theory voluntary much pressure had been exerted n them and the great majority joined unwillingly. Before joining they had killed their livestock, with disastrous effects upon the already low animal population of he Soviet Union. The authorities took fright at this, nd issued orders that pressure should be relaxed in the ecruiting drive, and that those who had been forced o join against their will should be allowed to leave. As result by September 1930 the proportion of families ad dropped to 21 per cent. It was then realised that the amage to the livestock population had already been one and that no softness to the peasant could bring ack to life the animals already slaughtered. So once 1ore pressure was applied and by 1931 53 per cent of easant families were members of a kolkhoz. By 1940 his number had risen to 97 per cent.

In spite of this virtual disappearance of the peasant olding, the battle between the Russian State and the ussian peasant was far from ended. By 1940 the peasant wned, to all intents and purposes, no land; but he still wned the majority of livestock, and he still, as a member of the kolkhoz, was allowed to cultivate some land, stensibly to provide food for himself and his family, ut in fact also for sale. This amount of land varied rom region to region: where the land was fertile he was llowed less; where it was poor he was allowed more. imilarly with livestock: in a predominantly arable district he could keep relatively few head of livestock; here the traditional farming was based predominantly n extensive livestock farming he could keep far more.

According to Bouvier (op. cit.), the nomadic people o
Central Asia were still, at that period, allowed to hav
as their own private property up to 10 horses, 8 camel
10 cows, and 150 sheep; whereas in a typical cereal are
the maximum was one cow, 2 calves, 1 sow, 10 sheep, an
unlimited poultry; and for cultivation $\frac{1}{2}$ hectare of land
While by 1940 only 700,000 horses out of 15 million wer
privately owned, in the same year nearly 55 per cent o
the cows, 57 per cent of the pigs, and 45 per cent of th
sheep were still in the hands of the peasants.

There are no published figures for that period to sho
what proportion of the total agricultural production o
the Soviet Union came from State farms or collectives
and what proportion came from peasant holdings. Bu
there is no doubt that the contribution that came from
private sources at the beginning of the Second Worl
War was still considerable. Yasny estimates, in *Th
Sovietized Agriculture of the U.S.S.R.* (Stanford Uni
versity Press 1949), p. 699, that in 1938 the produc
from individual members of collectives amounted t
3,200,000,000 roubles, while the payment for their wor
on the collective farms, which presumably bears a clos
relationship to the value of the product, and is unlikel
to be less than half and may well be two-thirds o
this value, totalled 2,400,000,000 roubles, in cash and i
kind (all figures at 1926 prices). If these estimates ar
accepted the peasants of the Soviet Union were still, i
1938, contributing between 40 per cent to 47 per cent t
the food production of their country.

The Government, therefore, in spite of having vir
tually abolished the private ownership of land, ha
failed to remove the peasant from his economicall
important position as the producer of a large part of th
food of the country. But this was not its only failure
It had also failed to bring about any significant increas

34

n food production. In fact, in many commodities the increase that was achieved was insufficient to keep pace with the rise in population, let alone to make it possible to bring about a rise in living standards. For example, in 1916 the cattle population of what is now the Soviet Union was 58·4 million: in 1940 it was only 47·8 million: pigs in 1916 were 23 million, and in 1940 22·5 million.

In arable crops the picture was somewhat brighter, though such increases as had taken place were less than might have been expected from technical advances alone, disregarding the supposed benefits of collectivisation. Thus wheat yields had risen by about 20 per cent from the 1913 level of 26·3 million tons to 31·7 million tons in 1940; and potatoes from 31·9 million tons in 1913 to 47·9 million in the 1938–40 average.

These figures give some indication of the problems facing any Communist government in its dealings with the peasant farmer. You can take a horse to water, but you cannot make him drink. You can, by education and propaganda, show the peasant the benefits he ought to get from being either a partner in a vast collective enterprise, or a wage-earner in a large, mechanised scientifically run farm. You can extol the benefits from a fixed salary, pensions when old, sick pay, increased yields arising from expert knowledge, the correct use of fertilisers and so on; easier work by harnessing machines; freedom from price fluctuations by prices fixed by the State: but till the peasant is more satisfied, and works harder, if he is free and independent.

In the sphere of arable production the problem is not unduly difficult. A system can be worked out, and has been on all collective farms on the Russian model and on many capitalistic farms also, whereby skilled work and productive work receive special bonuses on top of the standard rate of pay; and when the profit left over at

35

the end of the year, after all compulsory State deliveries have been made, taxes paid, and reserves set aside, is divided among all workers on the basis of the contribution of work that they have made. More important, and here the value of the earlier co-operative farms is seen, fertilisers, seed, and machinery can be distributed and allocated according to a centrally-controlled plan, so as to go to those enterprises where the best use will be made of them, while still allowing a considerable degree of autonomy to the co-operative farms themselves.

It is here that the true significance of the State Tractor Stations show their true value. The collective or co-operative farms can be left to a very great extent free of State interference, and with every appearance of self-government: but without machinery and fertilisers they can do nothing, and the machinery is all owned by the State Tractor Stations, and the fertilisers similarly allocated by the State. Thus, while giving the successor of the peasant the appearance of self-government and a large measure of independence, the Central Government is still in a position to direct the agriculture of the country.

As has been shown, even on the arable side, with all these advantages, the State by 1940 had made no great advances in the matter of yields. It had however succeeded in raising arable production and at the same time lowering, through mechanisation, the amount of labour employed on the land, though to a less marked degree than had taken place over the same period in many non-Communist countries. Thus by 1938 75 per cent of the land was ploughed by tractor, and all the grain reaped and threshed by machine, compared with the wooden plough, the sickle and the flail, which were all common in 1914. In place of the 25 million peasant holdings of 1928 there were, by 1940, 240,000 collective farms: and, more important than these changes, between 1926 and 1938, 24 million people had left the land and succeeded in finding work in the towns; while the countryside, with an absolute decline in rural population, was able to feed these town-dwellers at a still low, but rising, level of nutrition. This is an achievement which must not be underrated: no country can progress in its standard of living without a progressive decline in the proportion of its population that is occupied in food production. But the experience of other countries during the similar period suggests that the benefits of agricultural mechanisation and technical progress have been at least as marked where the peasant has been left free as where he has been coerced into collectivisation and co-operation.

But such success as the Soviet Union enjoyed in its agricultural policy up to 1940 was confined to arable production. The figures already quoted show its failure when it comes to livestock. And it must be remembered that livestock is an essential part of an improved standard of living. At the lowest levels of nutrition there is an absolute lack of calories, and the simplest means of making good this deficiency is by producing more for direct human consumption—more wheat, rice, maize, potatoes. But once this low level has been achieved the demand for animal products grows, for fats, meat, eggs and cheese. It must be the aim of every progressive government with the welfare of its people at heart to promote a system of agriculture where more of these animal products are produced. Livestock production requires individual care, and this the peasant will give to his own, but not to animals that are not his. Large-scale production can give certain advantages over livestock kept on the peasant scale, but even these cannot outweigh the benefits of the owner's eye, and in any case, they

37

can be provided by State help or co-operation to even the smallest producer. Thus in England today the smallest breeder of cattle can, by artificial insemination, have the use, at a very small fee, of the best bulls of whatever breed he chooses. He can also get, from government or private enterprise, expert advice as to the best and cheapest ration to feed his cows; and if he cares to join together with some of his neighbours he can buy those feeding-stuffs at a price just as low as can the largest consumer.

The fact is that agriculture, even in its more important livestock operation, is an intensive operation when compared with industry. It does not therefore adapt itself to the extensive techniques of industry, which are an essential part of the Soviet approach: and for this reason, if for no other, cannot, from the purely technical point of view, give of its best under such a system.

This weakness has been increasingly recognised since the end of the Second World War, and Khrushchev has been one of the leading Soviet figures most intimately connected with an attempt to overcome some of the shortcomings. Speaking to the Communist Party's Central Committee shortly after the death of Stalin, in 1953, he talked at length on 'Measures for the further advancement of agriculture' and referred especially to the acute shortage of meat and dairy produce, as well as of fruit and vegetables. He specifically mentioned that 'a disproportion had been in evidence between the rapidly growing requirements of the population and the level of production' (*Pravda*, September 15, 1953). This is incontrovertible evidence that the Soviet leaders themselves are dissatisfied with the progress of their agricultural policies.

Since 1945 further changes have taken place in Russian agriculture. Vast new areas beyond the Urals have been brought into cultivation, and although the yields from these huge tracts consistently fail to reach the planned targets, they have added significantly to the total production. Mechanisation has increased, and consequently it has been possible to release still more men and women from agriculture to work in the factories. Pressure on the peasant has been increased, and this has undoubtedly been made easier by the fact that a declining number of farmworkers were independent peasants in pre-revolution days. After all, a peasant of 25 in 1915 would be 65 in 1955, while the majority of collective farm workers at that latter date would have had no first-hand knowledge of the advantages and drawbacks of private ownership. Such resistance as they show now to collectivisation can come only from what they have heard from their parents of 'the good old days'—and, as we have seen, those days were far from good for the majority of peasants—and from such innate dislike as they may have to being a very small cog in a very big wheel, and such innate desire as they may have to run their own show.

But for all the increased pressure and the disappearance of the old pre-revolution peasant, private ownership of livestock was still recognised as having its importance. *Soviet Survey* of October–December 1958 states that 'The size of the plot [that may be cultivated by a collective farm worker for his own use] has been reduced from $1\frac{1}{4}$ acres ($\frac{1}{2}$ hectare) before the war to less than $\frac{1}{4}$ acre per family now. Simultaneously the private rearing of livestock has been handicapped by the increase in the minimum number of labour-days that have to be worked—by men, women, and children—in the collectives.' There is a further quotation from Khrushchev's agricultural speech already referred to: 'In the interest of increased livestock production Khrushchev had rebuked those in the Party who thought that "the productive livestock possessed by a collective farmer's household represents a danger to the Socialist system".' But he hastened to prophesy that the time will come 'when it will be unprofitable for the collective farmer to have livestock in his personal possession'. In spite of increased pressure, therefore, in some respects, the government still do not feel themselves in a strong enough position to bring too much force upon the peasant to abandon all private property.

In 1954 an ambitious programme was embarked upon with the object of increasing food supplies in the Soviet Union. This involved bringing into cultivation vast areas of the virgin steppes in the Kazakh region. Technically the problem did not present overwhelming difficulties. The soil was rich and the climate, although hard, favourable for growing cereals. Vast expenditure had to be undertaken in order to make roads and railways, not only for movement within the area, but also for bringing into the region the raw materials which were necessary for cultivation, and for taking out of the region the crops once they had been grown and harvested.

But above all, manpower was needed. A great propaganda campaign was embarked upon and the spirit of adventure as well as the patriotism of Russians was appealed to. It was not hidden that the new settlers would have to put up with many hardships at the beginning. 'To begin with we shall have to put up with cold heat and damp, live in tents, and renounce many amenities', said *Komsomolskaya Pravda* of February 25th, 1954. Although it was made clear that to begin with life would be hard, it was promised that before long conditions of life would improve. Many thousands of young enthusiasts volunteered and some middle-aged and older people were also attracted by promises that were made to give them a good life once the initial hardships had been overcome. These promises included long-term building loans of from 10,000 to 15,000 roubles, of which only 65 per cent had to be repaid, as well as temporary exemption from taxes and an increase of 15 per cent over the normal wages.

But as the years have gone by it was found that these building loans were of little value when building materials themselves could not be obtained; and that the tax reliefs and higher wages were insufficient to keep up with the local inflation that was caused by shortage of most consumer goods. From the agricultural point of view the scheme has been a success, though it has met with many difficulties, and at times crops that have been grown have not been fully gathered. But by the beginning of 1961, 41 million hectares of virgin land had been ploughed and a noticeable increase had been made to the food supplies of the Soviet Union.

But from the settlers' point of view the situation was far from satisfactory. This was made clear in Khrushchev's speech in June, 1961 at Alma Ata, the capital of Kazakhstan. In this speech he said, 'Comrades, I have been receiving many letters since my arrival in Alma Ata, and the main thing in these letters is the request for help in finding homes.' Settlers were still living communally in barracks and those who had freshly arrived had to spend many months in tents. An article in *Selkaya Zhizn* (Rural Life) of October 23rd, 1960, asks who is responsible for building operations in the virgin lands? Unsatisfactory supply of cement, slates, timber and glass, seriously delays building in the virgin lands .. this year the consumer co-operatives sold the following items to the collective farms in the northern oblasts of Kazakhstan: timber, thirty times less than required; cement, six times less; slates, seven times less; nails, five times less. Such supplies are dragging out building schedules for many projects by several years. . . . In the collective farms of Kustani Oblast this year, the following should have been built: 218 farms, 84 workshops, 73 buildings for cultural welfare establishments, 1,130 houses. In fact, only 15 farms, 4 workshops, 3 cultural welfare establishments and 150 houses were constructed. The total work plan was fulfilled by less than 10 per cent.'

It is not surprising that the enthusiasm of these pioneers is now waning, and that if it were possible for them to return to their former homes many of them would do so. Unfortunately for them, in the Soviet Union this alternative is not open to them. They have to remain where they are and hope that in due course not only will the agricultural production of this intrinsically fertile region help to solve the food problems of their country, but also that their own living conditions will before long become at least as supportable as they were in the farms and villages which they left behind them.

In 1956 Khrushchev introduced a major change in policy: this was the abolition of the Machinery Stations and the handing over to the collective farms themselves of the machinery which they required. For this change which aroused great controversy in the Soviet Union at the time, there are two reasons. The purely technical one is that when machines were scarce and only used for special operations it was more economical to have them centred at one Station where they could be serviced and maintained by skilled staff, and sent out to different farms as they were needed. To divide these machines up among the farms would not only mean less efficient maintenance, but also would mean that at certain periods a farm would have less machinery than it needed while at other times its machines would be standing idle as there was no work for them on that particular farm even though they might be needed elsewhere. But as the number of jobs that came to be done by machines increased, as, for instance, not only all ploughing, as opposed only to deep ploughing, came to be done by tractors instead of horses, and also lighter cultivations, grain sowing, fertiliser distribution, hay-cutting and so on; and as the supply both of tractors and implements increased, so it became possible for each individual collective farm to keep its machines fully employed, and to arrange for their proper maintenance.

But these purely technical reasons would not have been enough to warrant the disappearance of the Tractor Stations had not the management of the collective farms passed unquestionably into the hands of those who were politically reliable. For, as has already been said, in the early days of collectivisation, it was through the Tractor Stations that power was in fact exercised. By the mid-fifties, however, it was felt that this form of control was no longer needed, and that the management of the collective farms themselves could be relied on.

Now, after more than forty years of Communist rule, and after many variations, and sometimes even apparent reversals, of policy, agricultural production shows clear signs of rising. In some sectors the rise is marked; in others it is sluggish. Wheat, for instance, at 68·6 million tons in 1959 is 2½ times greater than it was in 1913: potatoes, at 86·4 million tons are between 2½ and 3 times as great. On the other hand pigs, at 48·7 million, are barely twice the 1916 figure of 23 million; and cattle have only gone up from 58·4 million in 1916 to 70·8 million in 1959, an increase of just over one-fifth.

Improved methods of cultivation and of plant and cattle breeding, the use of artificial fertilisers, mechanisation, the bringing into cultivation of formerly uncultivated land, all these have played a part. Undoubtedly they would also have played their part, as they have in non-Communist countries, had there been no Revolution. No one can say for certain that the success, under any other system of government, would have been greater or less. But of two things one can be sure. First, the Soviet Government has so far failed to evolve a system which, in the case of livestock, gives it the increase in production which it requires, but which does not at the same time involve a relatively high degree of private ownership, individual skill and responsibility, and personal reward. Secondly, so long as it is found necessary to retain this private sector of production the flame of private possession which burns in every peasant's heart will never be extinguished. How important a factor this will prove to be in the future remains to be seen. At this stage the fight is still on, and, depending on the need for food and upon the general tenor of public or governmental opinion, so will the freedom of the peasant within the limits of the kolkhoz rise or fall.

Many different views can be held concerning the success or failure of the Soviet Union agrarian policy, and it is still too early to pass final judgment. Yet some things are clear. The private ownership of land has virtually disappeared, and with it the use of hired labour by individuals in the cultivation of the land. In the place of the former peasant or serf have appeared workers who can almost be called a rural proletariat, men and women who are not in the main working directly for themselves, but whose reward is based upon the work they carry out. Some of these still will not co-operate wholeheartedly, some resist passively, and some are enthusiastic believers. I have met all these types on collective farms that I have visited in countries under Russian influence. On one occasion in Czechoslovakia I was being shown a collective farm and was asked what were the weekly hours of work on English farms. On replying 'Forty-seven' my guide exclaimed, 'Is that all?

But that's what comes of working for a capitalist boss. Why, on this farm we work 60 and even 70 hours if it's necessary. Here we aren't the type to be continually watching the clock.' At the next farm I was asked the same question. On my guard this time I answered that although the legal week was of 47 hours, at harvest time people worked 60, and even 70 hours. 'Ah well,' was the comment, 'that's what comes of being exploited by a capitalist boss: here our hours are limited by the State to 50.'

Undoubtedly working conditions have improved enormously from what they were in 1917—but then they have also in non-Communist countries. Undoubtedly also technical progress, especially on the arable side, has been great. Production has risen, the power of the land-owner remains—but today the landowner is the State rather than an individual. Russia is no longer a backward agricultural country with 90 per cent of its people living on the land: it is a progressive industrial country with a third of its population living in cities. Over 75 per cent of those over nine years old are literate. These are great achievements, but a great price has been paid for them. Above all, one thing emerges clearly. The problem of the land and of the men and women who work on it has been the greatest problem that the Soviet Union has had to face within its own borders, and it is a problem which even after forty years it has not succeeded in finally solving.

4

The Other States

TODAY Central and Eastern Europe consist of many
independent or nominally independent countries—
Poland, Czechoslovakia, Hungary, Yugoslavia, Rou-
mania and Bulgaria. In the Middle Ages the hegemony
of this same area was fought over and shared by three
great powers, Poland, the Ottoman Empire and the rising
Austrian Empire. Later, with the decline of Poland,
Russia extended its influence westward, while in recent
times, with the disappearance of the Ottoman and Aus
trian Empires, first Germany and then Russia played a
large part in the economic and political life of the area

It is therefore not surprising that both the form
and the timing of the agrarian evolution of this area
have varied, depending not only upon internal circum
stances, but also upon which of the great powers was, at
any particular time, in the ascendancy. In particular
during the period of Turkish overlordship those parts
subject to Turkish rule had an agrarian structure entirely
different from those which were part of the Austrian
Empire. But the path that has been followed has, par
ticularly in more recent times, been sufficiently of one
pattern to justify the treatment of all these countries as
a more or less uniform whole. It is not proposed to de
scribe the happenings in each country separately, nor to
deal in any detail with all the countries which today
make up Central and Eastern Europe. Instead, examples
will be drawn from some of them to illustrate the stages
of development through which most of them have at one
period or another passed.

Until the middle of the eighteenth century the feudal system in one form or another had continued unchanged and unchallenged, the nobles and the landowners exercising over their estates an absolute authority untrammelled by interference from the Imperial Court, no matter where it was situated. It was these feudal lords who provided much of the army with which the Hapsburg Emperors finally drove the Turks from Central Europe. As a result of this Croatia became a part of the Austrian Empire, and it was in Croatia that the earliest example of land reform in Central Europe is to be found.

The end of the wars against the Turks, and the opening of the Adriatic to ships other than those of Venice, led both to a general pacification of the area and to a great increase in trade. The former battlegrounds along the Croatian–Turkish frontier which had been uncultivated during the long war years now became settled and cultivated, the flow of trade brought fresh wealth to the district, and the bishops and nobles, released from the rigours of the Turkish wars, enjoyed the luxuries of peace in Vienna. There followed quickly the familiar pattern: the luxurious life of the city not only weaned the nobles from the more austere life on their estates among their own serfs, where, however remote from everyday life they might be in their castles, they were at least in a way members of the same community: it also increased their need for money. This money could only come from the sale of produce from their estates. They were no longer content with the labour dues and payment in kind which had sufficed when they lived on their own estates. More must be grown for sale, so more work was required from those on the land. Pressure was applied, as it was at different times throughout the whole of Europe in similar circumstances, causing discontent and hardship among the serfs.

But in Croatia the people who were being subjected to this pressure were not solely countrymen who, for generations, had done no more than till the soil, tend livestock and cut down trees; it was they and their fathers who had driven the Turks out of Croatia and they were still close to the battlefield. So they did not submit passively to the increased pressure for more work and more service on behalf of an absentee landlord. They resisted with force and in 1755, 20,000 men took part in the revolt of the Croatian Highlands. This was only crushed after the nobility had gathered together a full feudal army.

The cruelty and excesses of this army, as well as the fear of similar revolts spreading to other parts of the empire, led the Empress Maria Theresa to intervene. It was this intervention which may be called the first agrarian reform of Central Europe. Briefly these reforms specified and limited the duties and obligations of the serf, and interposed some form of central authority between the lord and his serfs, thus striking at the root of the thesis that a serf was no more than the chattel of his lord.

This same reform stipulated the area of the land which the serf held from his lord. This was fixed for example in Upper Croatia at 27 acres of arable land and 7 acres of meadow, and in Slovenia, where the land was poor, at 45 acres of arable land and 14 acres of meadow. The rent to be paid for this land was laid down and efforts were made to ensure that each holding was of the stipulated size. Those whose holdings were larger were forced to give up land to those whose holdings were too small; and if insufficient land could be found from such sources it was taken from forests which had been cleared or, as a final resort, from the lord's own demesne.

These changes, although a long way from the dispossession of the owners of large estates such as took place in many parts of Europe some 250 years earlier, were an interference with the rights of ownership, which was revolutionary at that time. Coming, as they did, some years before the French Revolution, they struck a sharp blow at the authority and power of the feudal landlord. Yet, paradoxically they helped to preserve the semi-feudal structure: for without them there might well have taken place at no very distant date in Austria those far more drastic changes that were soon to be seen in France.

In many parts of Central Europe, however, the former rigid structure of feudal society was maintained, though it was impossible completely to isolate the serfs from changes which were taking place in other parts of Europe. At the same time as the landowners were demanding increased exertions from the serfs, the serfs themselves began to see on the very distant horizon the faint glimmer of a different and a better life. This stimulated a general feeling of unrest, one of the symptoms of which was the revolt of 1830 in Russian Poland. This began as an uprising of army officers against Russian oppression, but it developed in parts of the country into a revolt of peasants and serfs against the landowners.

Shortly after this, in 1848, serfdom in Hungary was abolished, and those who had received land as tenants under the reforms of Maria Theresa now became freeholders. As in Russia, however, this did not lead to an automatic or immediate improvement in their economic position, nor was the influence or wealth of the landowner seriously diminished. In most cases the freed serf found himself compelled to work just as hard as ever for his former lord, and the wages he now received were used to pay the taxes which the State demanded in order to recompense the lord.

The lord himself was no worse off. He was no longer the legal owner of as many acres as before, but he had received cash compensation for these acres. He could no longer demand service from his serfs as a right, but for many years now that service had been grudging and unproductive. In its place he now had to pay for labour and could accordingly take steps to ensure that he got his money's worth; while he also had received cash compensation for the lost service, and with this money he could pay wages. Above all, he retained all his former demesne land, and now was able to exploit it on modern and commercial lines with selected paid labour in place of the grudging serfs.

Thus arose, after a very modest social and land reform, the post-feudal stage of society which characterised Central Europe in the nineteenth century and which persisted until the beginning of its disintegration after the First World War. Rural society consisted of a large number of small peasants, many of whom, as the years went by, became landless labourers, while a few acquired more land and wealth: and a small number of large estates farmed on commercial lines with paid labour by landowners who had a virtual monopoly of labour in their own particular region. This economic control over the lives of the workers and peasants proved no less effective than had feudal control. The main difference was that the economically fittest came rather more quickly to the fore, while the economically weakest went rather more quickly to the wall.

When the twentieth century began, it seemed throughout the whole of Europe as if change had come to an end and stability had been reached. The landowner had made concessions; he had submitted to the authority of the Courts of Law set up by a central government, he had relinquished legal control (though not economic control) over the lives of those who had been his serfs, he had adapted the use of his estates to the requirements of the times, and he had even consented to the payment of the same taxes as did any ordinary commoner. It was felt that these concessions, coupled with the opportunities that were available in the cities to the ambitious son of a peasant, or even to an agricultural worker, should act as an adequate safety valve for the release of such internal discontent as might arise.

This discontent which had been running through Europe from 1789 to 1848 had, it was felt, either spent itself or found a safe outlet, and the social order was now once more established for a further two or three centuries. The war of 1914 put an end to these dreams of stability; furthermore, the discontent which had prompted the peasant unrest in Croatia in 1750 and in Poland in 1830 was still there, and the shocks to which the whole of Europe was subjected by the First World War gave it a fresh opportunity to come to the surface. In spite of this the changes which took place after 1918 were slight compared with those that were to follow 25 years later, though massive compared with those that had gone before.

In Poland there was little alteration in the pattern of landownership or in the influence of landowners, whether lay or clerical. In the newly-formed republic of Czechoslovakia the old Bohemian aristocracy largely remained, though the rising importance of industry progressively diminished the political power of the landowner. In Hungary, after a short unsettled period, the landowner emerged still in possession of his vast estates and still providing those from whom political leaders were drawn. It was only in the new country of Yugoslavia that significant agricultural reforms took place.

Conditions and problems varied to a bewildering extent in this new country. In the north was Croatia, until

51

recently one of the suppliers of food to rich and industrialised Austria, now itself the most highly industrialised and richest portion of a poor and almost entirely agricultural nation. Most of the fertile parts of Croatia had belonged to, and had been farmed by, Austrian or Hungarian nobles who were now foreigners. To the south was Serbia, poor and backward except for the Banat and the Voyvodina, whose rich lands also had been largely owned by foreign nobles and yeoman farmers. Along the Dalmatian coast and in the mountains of Bosnia and Montenegro serfdom still existed.

Throughout this country promises of land had been made during the war to returning emigrants from America who had come to fight for their country, and to Slav prisoners from the Austrian army. Many of these prisoners returned from Russia full of enthusiasm for what they had heard had been done there in the matter of land reform. To these were added some 100,000 Serbian and Croatian peasants, now deserters from the Army, forming bands of revolutionaries in the mountains and forests. The new government had to bring these semi-outlaw bands back into the ambit of society, and the only way in which this could be done was by giving them land.

So came about another land reform in Croatia, this time extending over the whole area now forming Yugoslavia. First, all remnants of serfdom were abolished: and then between 1918 and 1933 a series of laws were passed, the object of which was to make land available for those to whom it had been promised. In the first instance this land came from the former large landowners, Hungarians and Austrians, most of whom had left the country when the new régime was set up; but there was not enough land from these sources. More was needed, and this had to come from the estates of those who remained.

This was obtained by setting an upper limit to the amount of land that might be owned by any one individual, the actual area varying with the type of farming and the fertility of the region. In all districts the upper limit was high: thus in Croatia it was 750 acres, and even more where justified by the existence of sugar factories or breweries. There was no question of trying to destroy large landowners as such, of breaking their power or of fulfilling the doctrine that the land should belong to those who till it. All that was hoped to achieve was to settle on the land those to whom land had been promised, and those who might otherwise attempt to overthrow the government by force: and at the same time to establish a class of politically-reliable peasant-proprietors.

These aims met with only partial success. Although in Croatia alone nearly 100,000 new smallholdings were set up, in most cases the 20 acres of land allocated to each family were not enough to ensure a reasonable standard of living. The remaining large estates too found production difficult, for the reform had been carried out with insufficient regard to local conditions and the need for buildings, so that some large farms found themselves with no barns or stables, while smallholdings were saddled with buildings adequate for an enterprise of a hundred times the size.

The result was that in the years immediately following the reform total agricultural production fell by 25 per cent (though by the beginning of the 1930's it had risen to a figure that was 27 per cent in excess of the 1914 level); while many of the holdings, especially those newly created, were sold by those who had been intended to become the stable backbone of rural society, but who found the life of an independent peasant too hard, and the rewards too slender. The buyers were in the main able, hard-working and ambitious Germans driven by land hunger from their own country, who later formed the German Volkdeutsch minority which, not only in Yugoslavia but also in Czechoslovakia, was to prove of such help to Hitler.

The long-term effects of this land reform in that part of Europe were never seen. The Second World War came too soon: and after 1945 it was followed by fresh and far more drastic upheavals in the countryside.

The agrarian reforms which took place throughout Central and Eastern Europe after the Second World War were imposed from outside, and were in no way an expression of the spontaneous desire of those most directly affected by them. But this does not mean that they were unpopular. The first reaction of the landless worker on hearing that he was to become the owner of some land himself instead of working, at a low wage, for another was naturally enough favourable. So was the reaction of the peasant proprietor of five acres on hearing that his holding was to be doubled by the addition of land from a larger farm. The large and prosperous peasant farmer was perhaps an object of jealousy, but he was not a natural enemy; but between the farmworker and peasant on the one hand and the landowner on the other there was a natural and age-long hostility which overrode most feelings of personal loyalty or respect. There was, therefore, not the opposition to the discomfiture of the landowner such as there might have been in countries where the bond between landowner, farmer and worker were close; especially when a direct result of that discomfiture was the apparent enrichment of the worker and small peasant.

The first objective of the Agrarian Reforms brought in after 1945 under the auspices of the Soviet Union was to break the power of the large landowners. The second was to gain the goodwill, at least temporarily until a

Communist government was firmly established, of the rural majority. The third was to make it possible to integrate agricultural production into an overall economic plan: and the fourth was to advance along the path of theoretical Communism, where the means of production should be communally and not privately owned, and where the countryside would be populated by a rural proletariat similar in all essentials to the proletariat of the cities. There were therefore different stages in the reform, each designed to achieve these various objectives.

The first was easy enough. No person was allowed to own more land than he and his immediate family could cultivate unaided. The upper limit varied from country to country and occasionally from district to district. In Yugoslavia this upper limit was 90 acres, though far smaller in more fertile areas, while the church, which included monasteries, convents and parish priests, were left with a maximum of 25 acres. Banks and other similar business institutions, which had formerly been extensive landowners, were entirely dispossessed.

In Hungary all owners of estates of 1,000 yokes (1 yoke = 1·4 acres) were dispossessed without compensation, while those who owned between 100 and 1,000 yokes were dispossessed of all but 100 yokes; these owners, however, received compensation in the form of non-transferable government securities, paying no interest for several years. In Poland all owners of estates of over 50 hectares (125 acres) were dispossessed, again without compensation. Those with less than 50 hectares were left undisturbed. The newly-created holdings were distributed in various sizes, depending upon the type of land, but usually covering about 5 hectares.

In all these countries individuals and institutions who were manifestly hostile to the new régime, or against whom there was any suspicion of having collaborated or sympathised with the Germans were deprived of all their property, even when there were insufficient grounds for bringing them before a tribunal as traitors. Many of these, especially the Volkdeutsch farmers on the western borders of Czechoslovakia and in the Yugoslavian Voyvodina, had already abandoned their homes and their land and moved westward to Germany before the advancing Russian armies. In Poland the removal westward to the Oder–Neisse line of the Polish–German frontier brought into Poland a large area of land until then owned and cultivated by Germans. These had all left, seeking refuge first in Berlin and later in Western Germany, so here too were hundreds of thousands of acres of unoccupied but until recently cultivated land.

Thus were these countries, in a matter of months after the end of the Second World War, rid of the influence of the great landowners who had controlled their destinies for the last thousand years. At the same time the new governments had at their disposal millions of fertile and well-equipped acres with which to achieve their second objective, that of gaining the goodwill of the rural population. It was, however, realised by those who had had previous experience of the break-up of large estates in Russia after 1917, that the small peasant holding was not only a far less efficient producer than was the large unit, but that it was far more difficult to ensure that the produce of the small farm found its way in adequate quantities to the cities than was the case with large farms.

These two points were brought home to me when travelling in those countries shortly after the land reform had taken effect. I had heard much of the heavy delivery quotas that were being exacted of the peasants, so, whenever I had a chance, I questioned them on this. One old Bulgarian farmer answered me in this way: 'Yes, it's true that we're supposed to deliver more milk and wool and grain to the town than we actually produce, but', with a grin on his face, 'it's a poor countryman who doesn't know how to hide a bit of his own crop from any government inspector.'

To such people this was nothing new. For generations they had succeeded in cheating the tax collectors, whether Turkish, Austrian or Russian; for generations they had outwitted, albeit in a small way, their landlord or his agent. All that was happening now was that they were carrying on with their old practices, but the enemy, the official to be duped, was different.

It was Károly Bárányos, Hungarian Minister of Agriculture at that time, who explained a further point to me in his imposing office in Budapest. I had asked him point-blank what the effect on production would be of the break-up of the large estates in Hungary, famous before the war for their high standard of agriculture. 'It cannot fail to be bad,' he said. 'The peasant is a hard worker, but he has no idea how to organise his work. When he was working on a large estate he was under orders. He was sent out to plant potatoes, to hoe sugar-beet, to feed the pigs, or whatever it might be, and he stayed at that job until it was finished because there was an overseer to see that he did. Now he's his own master. He flits from one job to another. He starts the day by ploughing; then he stops to milk the cow; he goes back to the ploughing, gets tired of that and cuts a bit of hay; and so on. Before he knows it the day is gone, but only half a day's work has been done. That's the way the peasant's mind works. I know,' he added, 'I'm a peasant myself.'

It was not only Bárányos who knew this. And that was why, in the different countries, care was taken not to distribute all the land that had been expropriated among the small peasants, land-workers and returning soldiers. They received some of it, but rarely was it enough to

57

bring their holdings up to an economic size. Many of them, too, were reluctant to accept land away from their own village. Polish peasants and workers from the east, whose villages had been incorporated into the Soviet Union were offered land in the 'recovered territories' of the West. But they were loth to settle there, both because of a natural reluctance to leave the countryside to which they were accustomed, and also because they did not believe that the former German owners would not one day return and drive them out. So, although many landless workers, smallholders, and tenants received a few acres under the land reform (in the People's Republic of Croatia nearly 100,000 families were thus benefited) much land, especially in Poland and Hungary, remained in the hands of the State, still run as large units, still in some cases administered by the same managers, though never by the previous owners. These owners, however, because of the shortage of men skilled in the administration of large estates, were at times employed on other State farms, provided their political background was not 'fascist' or 'reactionary'.

Since the Land Reform I have visited and stayed on many farms in Poland where the administrators have been fulfilling the same jobs as under the former noble owners. On some the manager had been an owner himself in the part of Poland which had now become Russian. In such cases he usually needed more than an absence of reactionary views: he had to have been a 'progressive' in pre-war days. I remember spending the night on an estate in south-east Poland run by such a man. We were having our evening meal in the large dining hall of the mansion, sitting at the high table, on a dais, with many of the estate workers at trestle tables below us. My host waved a thin aristocratic hand towards them as they sat there in their shirt sleeves, shovelling in the food, and said: 'I like to see people like that sitting there enjoying

58

themselves, in place of the bored men and women of fashion who used to eat here in the old days. But then I've always been a radical. How I shocked the countryside on the day I was married! The peasants gathered round the carriage as my wife and I drove away from the church, and I allowed them to kiss my hand—an unheard of thing for a peasant to touch the hand of a noble.'

Such managers rarely remained long at their jobs; so soon as qualified men with more reliable backgrounds could be found they were replaced. But whoever was the manager on the spot it was the State that retained control over the estates themselves and thus ensured that at least some of the country's agricultural land was cultivated in a reasonably efficient manner, and that the food that was produced from it could be used to feed the urban population.

But this did not go far enough. The power of the great landowner had been broken and he had disappeared from the countryside. But private property remained—there were even more property-owners than there had been before the reform—and the planning of agriculture as part of the national economy was even more difficult than it had been in the days of the large privately-owned estates. So came the next stage in the Reform. In the early days the slogan had been 'the land for him who tills it', and it was this that had gained the support of the worker and the small peasant for the revolutionary cause. There could be no direct or obvious retreat from this slogan. Yet it was essential that the peasant be liquidated. To this end the co-operative farm was instituted. Officials of the government travelled through the villages explaining the advantages that would come to the peasants if they joined together. They could then use machinery, and the State would help them to purchase it; they would have the use of well-bred stallions, bulls and boars, technical advice, good seed, artificia fertiliser, and all the other aids to successful farming which the large estate owners had enjoyed but which hitherto had been out of the reach of the small man They would, of course, retain their individual title to their land, and would be free to withdraw from the co-operative whenever they so wished. There would be no State interference; they would elect their own committee of management, and plan their own production; all the State would do would be to provide them with a technical expert to help them, advise them, but not control them.

Put this way the project sounded attractive, and those who found that owning land and farming it independently was not so easy or profitable as they had expected joined the co-operative. But many, particularly the larger or more successful peasants, were suspicious, and stayed out. Soon these independent spirits found life becoming harder for them. Their delivery quotas were increased such fertilisers and good seed as were available went to the co-operative, as did the machinery. If they persisted in their refusal to join, their delivery quotas were increased still further till it became impossible for them to fulfil them, and they were sent to gaol for their failure The fate of these brought the others into the co-operative and dissuaded those who were already members from leaving. These then found that the technical expert provided by the government to help them became in fact their general manager and political leader rather than their adviser on purely agricultural matters. Under his persuasion they renounced their individual rights as owners, the land thus becoming the joint property of the co-operative, or collective farm as it had now become Each member was given his task by the management committee, and paid according to the work he performed. At the end of the year the profit was, in theory, divided among the members according to the amount of work they had contributed. In fact, by the time taxes and interest on loans had been paid to the government and various compulsory contributions had been made, little was left over.

Thus was achieved, without violence and with little force, the third and fourth objectives of the Agrarian Reform. Private ownership of land was to all intents and purposes at an end, the peasant was now little different from the factory worker, and the central government could plan agricultural production on a national basis.

This, however, is not the end of the story. The peasant of Central Europe is no lover of feudalism, but equally he is no lover of the government, whether it be of the Right or of the Left. He wants for himself and his family as high a standard of living as he can get, but even above that he wants independence. He started fighting for it in the eighteenth century, and slowly he won concessions. In two hundred years, although still by Western European standards oppressed and downtrodden, he had made great progress. He was not prepared to submit meekly to a new form of aggression, especially when it came so soon after his apparent emancipation.

The peasants' resistance to the enforced collectivisation of the Communist régime is the outstanding example in modern times of the importance of the agrarian situation in politics. It will be many years before this struggle becomes history; for long it will remain part of the contemporary scene. But at the moment doctrinaire political thought is retreating before the unorganised empiricism of the countryside. The Polish and Hungarian rising of 1956 did not start on the farms and in no way could be called a Peasant Revolt. Yet had those two countries had a peaceful and prosperous rural population, had their farms been producing anything approaching that of which they were capable, had food in the cities been cheap and plentiful, as with the large area of fertile land which both countries had it should have been; in other words, had the Communists, after their original land reform, introduced a successful agrarian policy, those risings would in all probability never have taken place and, if they had, would never have met with such success as they did.

As it is there is at present in progress in these countries a move towards the appeasement of the peasant. 'You can push and you can shove, but I'm hanged if I'll be druv.' It is not the china pig of my childhood that is saying that, but the Slav and the Magyar peasant. Pushing and shoving has been tried and failed. It is not only in Bulgaria that the countryman knows how to hide his crop from a government inspector. To get something out of him a carrot is more effective than a stick. But how can a carrot be given to the peasant without weakening the whole basis of Communism, and without upsetting the balance between town and country, between industry and agriculture? If these countries are to prosper they must become more industrialised: yet an increase of industrialisation is impossible if agriculture offers a better life than does work in a factory.

Yugoslavia has taken the lead in this reversal of policy. Starting, because of its reforms which followed upon the First World War, farther along the road than did most of its neighbours in 1945, it pressed ahead with land reform, and by 1950 had reached its peak of collectivisation: but its declining agricultural production and its critical economic position could no longer be overlooked. First the formation of more collective farms was stopped, and later permission was given to members of existing collective farms to withdraw, taking with them their original holdings. The figures from Croatia give an indication of the readiness with which members availed themselves of this opportunity to leave. In 1950 there

vere in Croatia 1,560 collective farms with 270,546 members, farming a total of 735,000 acres. In 1954 (only a
year after co-operative farms had been allowed to dis-
band) there were 283 such farms with 17,040 members
farming just over 90,000 acres. By 1960 throughout the
whole of Yugoslavia 80 per cent of the land was privately
owned, 5 per cent was owned and cultivated by various
forms of co-operative, and State farms accounted for
5 per cent. What is more, the Government openly recognised the fact that the problem of the countryside
could be solved satisfactorily only with the goodwill of
the peasants. Thus not only did they leave them completely free to cultivate their land as they wished and to
market their produce in whatever way pleased them best;
but actively assisted them towards greater efficiency by
encouraging genuine co-operation, for instance, in the
ownership of machinery and the purchase of fertilisers.

Furthermore, although the State farms had first call
upon the supply of such aids to better farming as new
high-yielding seeds, once these demands had been met the
private peasant farms were encouraged to make use of
them. By this means not only did the Government begin
to gain the respect and confidence of the peasant, and the
standard of living in the countryside rose, but the agricultural output of the country increased strikingly, so that
in 1959, for the first time since before the Second World
War, Yugoslavia had a significant exportable surplus of
agricultural produce. For example, the wheat crop which
in 1938 was 3·06 million tons fell in 1950 to 1·83 million;
by 1959 it was nearly 4 million tons. In 1938 maize was
·8 million tons, dropping to 2·09 in 1950, and rising to
·67 million tons in 1959. Cattle in 1931 totalled
·7 million head and had, somewhat surprisingly, risen
slightly to 5·3 million in 1950; and by 1960 there were
still 5·3 million. Pigs, as might be expected, responded
to change more rapidly. In 1950 these had fallen from

the 1931 figure of 4·6 million to 4·3 million; but by 196●
they had increased nearly 50 per cent to 6·2 million.

For all this the Government made no secret of it
desire for the disappearance of all privately-owned
property: but now, instead of attempting to achieve thi
end by force it publicly proclaimed that it could only b●
achieved with the agreement of the peasants. This agree
ment could be obtained only when the peasant came t●
realise that his standard of living would be higher an●
his mode of life more comfortable if he were an employe●
either on a State farm or in a factory than if he remaine●
a small independent farmer on his own land. With thi●
end in view factories were built in the larger marke●
towns and the provision of good houses for factor●
workers was given priority. The hope now is that as th●
years go by an increasing number of peasants will ex●
change the long hours in the fields in all weathers, an●
the uncertainty inevitably connected with small-scal●
farming, for the security and relative comfort of a well
paid factory job and the amenities which go with livin●
in the town.

Already by 1960 it had been possible to reduce th
proportion of workers in agriculture from the pre-wa●
figure of 80 per cent to 50 per cent and it is hoped tha●
in another 20 years this will be further reduced to 20 pe●
cent. This reduction in rural manpower will make ●
vastly increased labour force available for industry; whil●
agricultural mechanisation, made possible because of th●
larger scale of the enterprise, will enable this greatl
reduced agricultural labour force to produce even mor●
food than is being produced by double the number o●
workers at the present time.

In other countries under Russian influence the change
have not been so great. For one thing in none of them
was collectivisation pushed to such lengths as in Yugo
slavia; for another, governments have been unable t●

swallow the unpalatable fact that, at least as a temporary measure, the private ownership of land is essential to the production of food until such time as the peasant has become convinced that he will be better off in some other job. For all that the fact of private ownership has been accepted, however grudgingly, as has the importance of the profit motive for the cultivator. The principles that remain are that no man should own more than he and his family can cultivate personally but that with this land he can do what he likes: and that where, for economic reasons, large estates are desirable, they should be owned by the State, and that the State should retain the responsibility for the actual cultivation.

But the peasant in these other countries is not happy. He knows that he is there only on sufferance, and that sooner or later he will be liquidated, either by direct State action or by the force of economic circumstances. It remains to be seen whether the other countries of Eastern Europe follow the lead of Yugoslavia and ease the path of the peasant from his uneconomic smallholding to the better paid factory job: or whether they will wait for a propitious moment and then compulsorily absorb his holdings into a large State enterprise.

5

Germany

Germany today is two separate countries: one part has
an economy organised on Communist lines, while the
other carries on with the more traditional Western
European system. But the background of these two areas
is essentially similar. True, Germany only became a
single country comparatively recently, in the middle of
the nineteenth century, but for long before that the
methods of government and of land ownership were in
general similar throughout the whole area. Just as
Prussia became the leader in the eventual unification of
Germany, so was the example of Prussia, before the
unification, of importance to many neighbouring king-
doms and grand-duchies. A description of the agrarian
development of Prussia is therefore of use in obtaining
a general background of the whole area which was later
to become the German Empire.

Prussia in fact was originally colonised by the Teutonic
Knights in the thirteenth century. These Knights were
not interested primarily in acquiring riches for themselves nor were they interested in cultivating the soil.
They were thus content to leave these activities to others
while they concentrated upon their aim of spreading the
Christian faith by means of their profession, which was
fighting. For this reason Prussia did not pass through a
period of feudalism as it is known in other parts of
Europe; indeed, for long much of the political and
economic power in that area was to be found in the
hands of the burghers of the Hanseatic League, while the

andowners had little influence outside their own imme-
liate estates.

It was not until the end of the fifteenth century that
:he country nobility finally emerged victorious from
heir struggles with the cities of the Hanseatic League.
They began then to consolidate their powers and their
:conomic importance by the gradual introduction of
.erfdom, which until then had been unknown in Prussia.
On the other hand, the other States which later were to
'orm together to create modern Germany were following
:he feudal form common at that time in Western Europe.
This left the Prussian landowners as the sole group to
whom the territorial princes could look for financial
.upport and in return for this support they were granted
:ver-increasing powers. In Brandenburg the Margrave
Joachim II made repeated concessions to the nobles in
'eturn for financial aid, and with this support the nobles
ncreased their control not only over their own peasants
)ut also over the burghers in the neighbouring cities.

Thus while in England feudal services were giving way
o paid labour, and the mercantile interests were taking
)ver some of the powers of the landowning nobility, in
'russia the reverse process was taking place. The Prussian
andowners, throughout the centuries, consolidated their
)ower, and right into the nineteenth century continued
o deal with their own estates, and those who worked on
hem, as they wished. While in certain matters they
ecognised the authority of the Central government, on
heir own estates they allowed no interference, retaining
:ven the right to forbid their workers to leave the estate,
)r to marry without permission, and retaining also the
)ower of life and death over them.

The spread of more democratic forms of government in
Germany, the rise in the Ruhr and elsewhere of the
)owerful industrial and banking class, even the abolition
)f serfdom in 1810, still left the Prussian landowner in

fact, if not in theory, with absolute power on his own
estate, with economic and political pre-eminence in his
district and even his country, and above all with an in-
grained and unquestioning belief in his own superiority.
It was this conviction of his own intrinsic worth which
was looked on, perhaps with dislike and even with dis-
approval, but undoubtedly with envy, by every section
of the new Germany of the nineteenth century. To many
the epitome of the best type of German was the Prussian
Junker as shown in novels and films—tall, of military
bearing, arrogant, rigid, disciplined, a man brought up
from earliest childhood in the knowledge that the people
on his estate though not legal serfs, were there to serve
him and to obey and that his role in life was to command.
Even the fact that others in Western Germany had more
money than he had, or that some, in the South, had
longer lineage and more quarterings, did not shake his
belief in himself and his class. His estates still brought
him in the money he needed, he still had servants to wait
upon him, and he came from a long line of landowners,
that was enough for him. It was enough, too, to spread
his influence in all matters pertaining to the land
throughout the rest of Germany, even where industry
and banking held economic sway.

This attitude of the Prussian landowner persisted even
after two world wars and social upheaval. Shortly after
the Second World War I visited a farm in the British
Zone of Germany on the North German plain owned by
a Prussian of the old school. Although talk of land reform
was very much in the air, and although only a few miles
away in the Russian Zone all large estates had already
been liquidated, although his country had been defeated
and was now occupied, his attitude remained unchanged.
Accompanied at a respectful distance by the farm overseer I was being shown the stables, and enquired about
some pieces of harness. The owner ordered the overseer

o fetch it for me to see. He set off at a brisk pace but that was not enough. 'Run!' shouted the Junker, as if on the barrack square, and obediently as his father and grandfather had done before him, the overseer ran.

Here is seen the corollary of the Prussian landowner. It is not enough that he gives orders with the knowledge that these orders will be unquestioningly obeyed. There must also be a group of people who do, in fact, obey unquestioningly. In an almost entirely agricultural society where holdings consist of very little other than large estates, where there are few peasants or small tenant farmers, there is little opportunity for the farmworker to escape from his dependence upon the landowner. A few of the more adventurous escape, but the vast majority remain, steeped in the tradition of absolute obedience and unconscious of the wider opportunities that await them elsewhere.

It was the combination of these two groups, the one giving orders, the other obeying, that enabled the Prussian landowner to weather for so long the winds of change that blew upon Europe with the advent of industrialisation, and even to weather the storms that followed upon the defeat of Germany in 1918. The social structure of the German countryside remained essentially unaltered, as did the form of landownership. In the North the large estate still predominated, usually in the hands of old families. It became somewhat easier for the farm-workers to find work in the towns, but the movement of labour from the land to the factories was not fast, and mechanisation made it relatively easy for the landowner to maintain production even with a smaller labour force. More important, it made it possible for him still to retain his attitude towards the farmworker, which he could not have done had he begun to suffer from a shortage of labour.

The world economic depression at the end of the 1920's

hit German agriculture hard: but the landowners of the
North, whose livelihood depended to a great extent on
the large-scale production of arable crops—wheat, rye,
potatoes and sugar-beet—and on pig-fattening, still had
sufficient political power to force the government to enact
special measures for the protection of these crops.

Even under the Nazi régime there was little noticeable
change: and though there was much about Hitler and his
policies that was unpalatable to the German landowner,
his policy of self-sufficiency, and of 'blood and soil' had
a strong appeal to them. As a result of Hitler's deliberate
drive towards producing as much food as possible from
German soil, production rose so that by 1939 Germany
was producing 85 per cent of its food requirements at
home.

When the end of the Second World War came in 1945,
the Russian armies were in occupation of a large part of
Prussia. By agreement with the Western Allies they
eventually took control of all that land lying south of
the Baltic, which includes some of the most fertile areas
of Germany, as well as the great arable estates of the
North German plains. The agreed policy of the Allies
was to remove from positions of power and importance
all those who had in any way been connected with the
Nazi régime. This entailed the expropriation of many
estates, since their owners had been supporters of Hitler,
but the Russians went farther than that, and, during the
first few months of their occupation, introduced a Land
Reform which forbade any individual to own more than
50 hectares. Since most of the farms and estates in the
Russian zone of Germany were large ones, the great
majority of holdings came under this reform.

The immediate result was disastrous upon food production. Already ravaged by war, with many landowners
and farmers already fled to the western zones where they
had fewer fears for their fate, with buildings, livestock

and machines destroyed by fire and bombardment, this great agricultural area was producing only a fraction of its former yields. Now Land Reform discouraged those who might otherwise have remained and worked to rebuild their farms. The workers and refugees from German areas of Poland and Czechoslovakia were incapable of the management of their new holdings, and in any case were handicapped by lack of livestock and machinery, as well as seed and fertiliser. Furthermore, such was the need for food in the cities that heavy delivery quotas were imposed upon them, which they were frequently unable to fulfil.

Thus instead of a feeling of gratitude towards the occupying forces who had given them land, and a willingness to co-operate with them, there quickly grew up a mistrust and a desire to do all in their power to retain as much as they could of their crops to consume themselves or to sell at huge prices on the black market, instead of handing them over at low controlled prices to the authorities.

It was not long before the official policy changed. Instead of setting up tens of thousands of smallholdings, privately owned, the existing owners were encouraged, and even forced, into co-operative farms or State farms, known respectively as Landwirtschaftliche Produktionsgenossenschaften (LPG), or Volkseigene Gueter (VEG).

The State farms (VEG) originated in 1945 after all holdings exceeding 100 hectares had been confiscated without compensation. By 1960 these farms covered approximately 6 per cent of the total agricultural acreage. The co-operative farms (LPG) were brought into being in 1952, and by 1960 accounted for 84 per cent of the total agricultural acreage. Members of these co-operatives were allowed to keep from their original holdings a plot of up to half a hectare and in certain cases two cows, two breeding sows, five sheep, and poultry.

The land which each member brought with him when

he joined the co-operative still remained in the land register as his property: but he might sell his land only to the co-operative itself, to a member of the same co-operative, or to the State: and at all times the use of the land was vested entirely in the co-operative. No payment was made for the land which the farmer brought into the co-operative when he joined but it was taken into account in the payment made at the end of the year for the work done. Up to 40 per cent of the surplus of the income of the co-operative could be used for these payments.

Thus it is clear that the general pattern already seen in the Soviet Union and in other countries under its control has been followed pretty closely in the eastern zone of Germany.

In the western zones a different policy was pursued. In theory all traces of Nazi influence were removed, though there is no doubt (and this also happened in the Russian zone) that many former Nazis were able to retain both their possessions and their positions. A relatively small number of large estates were broken up: but as the great majority of large estates were to be found in the Russian zone this was not of great significance. Otherwise the agrarian structure was left intact, apart from the repeal of certain specific laws introduced by Hitler. Food production in the western parts of Germany, therefore, had to make good the ravages of war, but did not at the same time have to adapt itself to any very great changes either in the system of landownership or in the people who were actually growing the food, or the conditions in which they worked.

Here, then, are two very different methods of dealing with the agrarian problem in one country, both sections of which have an identical historical and economic background. Which of them has been the more successful? Both on the economic and on the personal side there are statistics available which help us to arrive at an answer.

Before the Second World War what is now Eastern Germany was not only the main agricultural producing area of the country, but also enjoyed the most advanced agriculture. As the following table shows, with the exception of the gross yield of sugar beet East Germany consistently outyielded West Germany. In the five-year period 1954–1958 the roles were reversed, and in every case a decline is found in East Germany while the West gives a marked rise in yields, so that it is now outyielding the East in all main commodities. This improvement is not confined to crops alone but is shown in most of the livestock products. Thus in 1958 the average annual yield of cows in the western zone was 3.41 tons of milk compared to 2.68 in the eastern zone: the average live weight of cattle in slaughterhouses was 492 kilos in the West compared with 360 in the East: and only in the case of pigs was the East superior with a yield of 122 kilos compared with 112 kilos for the West.

West Germany—East Germany Agricultural Yields

	West		East	
	1935–39	1954–58	1935–39	1954–58
Grains (*tons per hectare*)	2.26	2.67	2.42	2.25
Potatoes (*tons per hectare*)	18.77	22.25	19.84	15.10
Sugarbeet (*tons per hectare*)	33.14	35.55	30.94	26.45
Sugar content (%)	12.9	13.6	14.3	12.6

There can be little doubt therefore that on the economic side the system followed by the West for promoting agricultural production has proved superior. But, as has been said in the first chapter, economic results are not enough. Even the most outstanding material improvements are not worth while if the people themselves are unhappier. A fair indication of contentment with the state of affairs is given by the number of Germans who move from the eastern zone to the western, and vice versa.

There are no completely reliable figures for movements in both directions since the end of the war, but it is probable that between the end of the war and the end of 1960 over $3\frac{1}{2}$ million Germans came from the east to the west, and during the three years 1958–1960 approximately 550,000 made this journey. In the same three years the movement in the opposite direction was about 150,000.

It thus seems clear that not only has the western zone a more efficient system of agriculture, but it is also succeeding in bringing about greater contentment among its population than is the eastern zone.

6

China

As one of the two leading Communist countries, China should give valuable help in our quest for knowledge concerning the results of Communist methods in agriculture and the countryside. But a country of the vastness of China, with its 600 million inhabitants, its range of climate varying from tropical to near-polar, its soil from arid steppe to rich river valley, and its people from primitive nomad tribes to highly civilised town-dwellers with the history of the oldest civilisation in the world behind them, cannot offer any quick, black or white, answer to our question. Furthermore, it will be remembered that even after more than forty years of Communism Russia is still searching for the best means of implementing Communism in the countryside, and the results to be seen there are still insufficiently clean-cut to permit of only one interpretation. Communism only came to a relatively peaceful and unified China some fifteen years ago, so any conclusions which are drawn from the results to be seen there today can only be regarded as very tentative.

That area of China which is agriculturally and economically important differs from those countries which we have already described in that at no recent date has the large-scale ownership of land been an important factor in the life of the countryside. There were, of course, until the seizure of power by the Chinese Communist forces, certain areas where a tribal chief still held sway, and others where large tracts of cultivated land were in the ownership of one individual. But throughout

75

those areas where the greatest density of rural population was to be found, and from which came the greatest quantity of China's food, the system was predominantly one of small owners operating their land by share-cropping.

Now share-cropping can mean many things. At one end of the scale, as in parts of France, it is a matter of carefully regulated contract between owner and cultivator. The owner surrenders his possession of an area of land for a fixed period, perhaps 7 or 14 years, to the cultivator who, within wide limits, has complete freedom to cultivate as he sees best, supplying his own seeds and fertiliser his own machinery, and perhaps even employing paid labour to help him. In return he pays every year to the owner of the land an agreed proportion, perhaps 10 or 15 per cent, of the crops that he harvests.

At the other end of the scale, and this system is frequently still found in many countries of the Middle East the share-cropper is no better than a labourer whose pay is only received at the end of the year, and which depend upon the value of the crop. Here the landowner, acting most frequently through an agent, arranges with a peasant family for them to cultivate an acre or two of his land. The owner decides what crop is to be grown, and provides the seed—and the fertiliser if the agriculture of the district is sufficiently advanced to use it. The share-cropper and his family cultivate the soil either with primitive hand tools or perhaps with a simple plough drawn by their own donkey; they sow the seed by hand weed the crop and harvest it by hand. It is then brought to the owner's threshing floor where it is threshed under the supervision of the owner's agent. He then sells it, and hands over to the share-cropper perhaps one quarter or one third of the money received. But as the share-cropper has had no money for his needs during the past year he is very possibly in debt to the owner, who therefore

ubtracts from the amount due the debt and the high
nterest charges payable on it. If the harvest has been a
ʙad one there may be nothing left over for the share-
ʳropper who therefore is forced to continue the so-called
ʙartnership on perhaps even less favourable terms for
ʰe ensuing year.

In China the most usual system of share-cropping was
ᵒomewhere between these two extremes, but considerably
ᵑearer the latter. The landowners were usually small
ʙroprietors living in the village, or in a neighbouring
ᵗown. They did not interest themselves in agriculture
ᵃnd took no part in improving techniques or increasing
ʸield. Since land was scarce and cultivators many they
ᵛere able to extract harsh terms from those who knew of
ᵑo other way of maintaining themselves than by working
ᵒn the land. The lion's share of the crop from the tiny
ʙarcels of land that each family cultivated on this share-
ᶜropping basis went to the landlord who, owning at least
ᵉeveral plots, was able to live in comparative affluence
ᵛithout doing a stroke of work. The balance had to sup-
ʙort the share-cropper and his entire family. As in the
Middle East this was frequently insufficient, with the
ʳesult that he became indebted to his landlord who thus
ʙecame yet richer.

This was one of the problems facing the new Chinese
ℂommunist government when it came to power. The
ᵉecond was that of flood control and irrigation. Most of
ℂhina's agricultural production takes place in the fertile
ʳiver valleys where the land is deep and rich from the
ᵒoil that has been washed down from the hills over
ᵗhousands of years of erosion. But at times these rivers
ᶠlood, and carry away crops and top-soil, leaving the
ᶜultivators cropless for a whole year. At other times the
ᶠlow becomes a trickle, leaving insufficient water for
ʳrrigation during the hot, dry summer: and again the

crop fails and famine ensues. Had there been great land owners in these parts of China, men not only of wealth but also of vision and resource, schemes of flood control and irrigation might have been worked out. Had the government been made up of statesmen with a knowledge of the countryside, and an interest in the welfare of the people living in it, the government itself might have undertaken such work: but as it was, nothing had been done, and every year or so great areas of China's most fertile agricultural land was cropless and poverty-ridden to an even greater extent than usual as a result of either too much or too little water.

When Mao-Tse-tung took power he was faced with a different and more difficult problem than were the leaders of the Russian revolution some thirty years earlier. Four out of every five inhabitants of China lived in villages, three out of every four were actively engaged in food production, there was no nucleus of industrial workers on whom to count for support whether in political or economic innovation: and there were no great landowners the liquidation or dispossession of whom would serve as a focus for land reform and re-distribution. In place of having to deal with a relatively few rural magnates the new Chinese Communist government had to deal with several hundred small landowners in every village. None the less Mao followed the habitual Communist custom of promising that the landowner would be abolished and that the land would belong to those who cultivated it.

In a few years Mao's promises had been implemented, and the former share-croppers became owners of their own land, though, in order to achieve this, yet more brutal methods were required, because of the larger numbers of small landowners than were found in other Communist countries, even including Russia. But, as in other countries, this did not solve the problem. Water-control was untouched, and apart from this no more food was produced. In some areas the new owners had rather more to eat, but then there was still less for the already undernourished towns. Where this did not happen the peasants were no better off than they had been before, being oppressed now by government officials instead of the landowner.

It was in 1950 that the peasants received their land, and they were then encouraged to work together by the setting up of Mutual Aid Teams in the villages. In this way it was hoped that not only would cultivation be more efficient and yields higher, but that the advantages of co-operation would become apparent to the peasants themselves. The Mutual Aid Teams, with a strong political flavour, and under the leadership of Party members in each village where they operated, reached a total of over seven million by 1955: but in spite of propaganda and much political help, they were not sufficiently effective to bring about an increase in production great enough to satisfy the government: nor were they sufficiently attractive to encourage the peasants voluntarily to merge their newly-acquired land in co-operative farms. So, in 1955, compulsory co-operation was introduced, and by the end of that year 633,000 so-called co-operative farms had been set up. This number increased to 784,000 by 1957, but once more the rate of advance was not fast enough for the authorities. More drastic steps were needed to abolish all idea of private property and enterprise in the countryside and to introduce true Communism throughout the length and breadth of China. This involved the disappearance of the so-called voluntary village co-operatives, and the welding together of all village activities into communal effort.

This was something far more drastic than anything that had hitherto been attempted. In 1958 the system of rural communes was introduced. This meant the setting-up of Communism in its most literal sense in the villages. Private property was entirely abolished so that ownership was restricted to the most simple of personal possessions and the whole of the village community was combined into one group working for the community's economic advancement. The Commune became responsible for agriculture and also for industry, trade, education, and even the militia. Not only did all property, animals and tools (excepting houses, furniture, clothing and bicycles) become the property of the community, wives no longer cooked for their husbands, since all food was provided in the central mess halls: mothers no longer cared for their children but sent them instead to the Commune's nurseries and schools so that both parents would be free to work on the land or in the factory, making roads, or serving in the militia.

This drastic reorganisation started less than ten years after each tenant or farm worker had been given his own small plot of land and allowed to cultivate it as his own in place of as a tenant of the local landowner. It was heralded by the Chinese press and by political propagandists as solving all rural problems. In particular water control could now be effected. The central government could undertake the large-scale planning of whole watercourses and river valleys, and, where necessary, provide capital and technical knowledge. The labour brigades of each commune, working for the good of their community and under central direction, would supply the manpower.

In the autumn of 1958 the *People's Daily* announced that the irrigation and water conservancy projects which had already been accomplished had disposed for ever of the danger to agriculture from flood and drought. Optimistic forecasts were made of the fantastic yields that would be harvested in 1958 as a result of the reorganisation of the countryside. This optimism was fed not only by the need to enthuse the peasants themselves, many of whom had not taken kindly to the change, but also to justify the officials who had planned the new system, and to encourage those whose task it had been to carry out the plans: furthermore, it was fed by exceptionally favourable weather.

The harvest of 1957 had already been a good one, yielding 185 million tons of grain (which in Chinese statistics includes pulses and the grain equivalent of potatoes). This was enough to maintain the monthly rations (rationing had been introduced in 1953, three years after the land reform) at 40–60 lbs. for working men, and 30 lbs. for white-collar workers. It was forecast in February 1958 that the harvest would reach 196 million tons, or 5 per cent more than in the previous year. By August this estimate had been raised to between 300 and 350 million tons, and by December it had reached 375 million tons, or twice that of the previous year.*

These figures impressed Western students as well as the Chinese themselves. Dr. Biekl of the Institute of World Economics of Kiel University wrote in *World Economy* (December 1958)—'Nothing convinces more than success. The burden which the Chinese cultivator had to accept in accordance with the Party's doctrine was immense. Now the results are there for everyone to see. Any resistance that may have existed among the rural population is thus likely to have lost its ground.' And a year later, when signs were already appearing that all was not well with China's food supply, Dr. de Castro, the Brazilian authority on world food problems and author of *The Geography of Hunger,* was quoted by Irvine in *Phantom Food in Communist China*† as saying in 1959,

* Communist China's Agricultural Calamities: *The China Quarterly* No. 6, April/June 1961.
† *Asian Survey*, Vol. 1, No. 1. Berkeley, California. March, 1961.

that 'New China's victory over the eternal plague of hunger is as startling an event as the conquest of inter-planetary space.'

By the spring of 1959 it was clear that the estimates of the previous year were a long way off the target. By August 1959 the figure for the previous year's harvest was officially given as 250 million tons, but there is little reason to think that those statistics rested on any firmer base than did the earlier ones. In view, however, of the exceptionally favourable weather, and taking into account the dislocation, discontent, and inefficiencies that were bound to follow upon the creation of the com-munes, a harvest some 20 per cent greater than that of the previous year, or about 220 million tons, seemed to be well within the bounds of probability.

Optimistic forecasts were again made for the 1959 harvest, and again the same reasons were present for these exaggerations. But this year the weather was not so kind, nearly one-third of the sown area suffering from drought or flood, compared with one-sixth in 1958. In spite of this a forecast of 10 per cent in excess of the previous year was made, and this was not changed although serious shortages were reported from both towns and rural areas. Undeterred by this, the target for 1960 was once more fixed at 10 per cent above the harvest of 1959. But towards the end of the year it became im-possible to disguise the crop failures in many areas. The weather was described as being the worst for a hundred years. Almost every province was affected by drought and 20 provinces were hit by floods and typhoons. Altogether it was reported that 60 million hectares of land suffered. But just as it is clear that the optimistic forecasts for the 1958 and 1959 harvests were exaggerated, so it may well be that the disasters of 1960 were also magnified, partly by a natural human tendency to see things either as high success or abysmal failure, but also as a fresh means of stimulating cultivators to still greater efforts, without placing blame either on government policy or government officials.

To add to these official accounts of difficulty and failure came the stories of refugees from the communes, naturally only too anxious to expose the failure of a system to which they were bitterly opposed. But a sense of proportion is introduced into the problem by an interview with Chou-En-lai by Edgar Snow,* when the harvest of 1960 was described as less than those of 1958 and 1959, and more than that of 1957. It was thus probably between 190 and 200 million tons, which should be sufficient to feed at a low level a population of about 650 million people. The chances are that the average consumption in China in 1960–1961 was somewhat under 2,000 calories a day, or 15 per cent less than it was thirty years earlier, before the Japanese invasion. Low though that is, and deficient in many of the essentials for full health, it is still no worse, and quite possibly somewhat better, than that of many other Asian countries.

The fact remains, however, that China has so far failed to solve her agricultural problem, and that, at the best, the Chinese of 1961 is no better fed than was the Chinese of 1951 or 1941. What is more, the Chinese government seems to have recognised the fact that, in spite of its ambitious Twelve Year Agricultural Programme, large imports of food will be needed for many years ahead. This programme runs from 1956 to 1967 and envisages an overall increase in food production of 150 per cent, the trebling of the cotton output, and a rise in grain from the 1955 total of nearly 180 million tons to 450 million tons in 1967. When it is remembered that by 1960, nearly half way through the programme, grain production had probably barely reached 220 million tons, a

* A Report from Red China: *Look*, January 31, 1961.

figure of 275 million tons for 1967 would seem to be far more realistic.

The technical, as opposed to the political, basis of this programme was control of water, by drainage and irrigation, and its failure in the initial years is shown by the havoc wrought in the 1960 crops by drought and flood. This failure is hardly surprising in view of the emphasis placed by the Chinese economic planners, in this respect no different from Communist planners in other countries at similar stages of economic development, on industrial investment. In fact only one-tenth of all public investment was set aside for agriculture and forestry, and of this already inadequate total only two-thirds was to be devoted to water control: while from the remaining one-third had to come money to cover mechanisation, fertilisers, research, education, land reclamation, afforestation and the countless other activities that are essential when any substantial progress is to be made on the road from primitive to modern agriculture.

The targets of the Twelve Year Programme have not been renounced; and there is as yet no open retreat from the principles of the communes. But the Chinese government has accepted the fact that for the years ahead China will be unable to produce within her own borders enough food for her needs. Contracts have now been signed mainly with Australia and Canada, for 10 million tons of wheat to be delivered between 1961 and 1963: and the Soviet Union has supplied half a million tons of sugar.

But more significant than these imports of food is the change of emphasis, again paralleling what is seen in most Communist countries at the comparable stage of development, away from communal ownership and back towards restricted private ownership, or to ownership in the smaller unit of the 'brigade'. In an article in *Red Flag* published early in 1961, the Minister of Agriculture, Liao Lu-yen, wrote that in place of the communes the production brigade (formerly the collective farm) was to form the basis of farm management at the present stage of development. 'Draught animals, farm tools and the other principal means of production belong to the production brigade and the products of the brigade are at our disposal. . . . The transition from the present system of commune ownership is a matter for the future.'

Even more significant is the fact that individual members of the commune are now being actively encouraged to produce on their own, as a side-line to their activities as members of the group. Each family has a private plot of land on which it may grow vegetables and keep livestock not only for its own consumption, but also for sale at free-market prices. At the same time bonuses are paid in kind, which may also be sold on the free-market, to production brigades as an incentive to individual brigade effort.

Thus, once more, in Communist China as in other Communist countries, we see a retreat in the face of economic necessity, from the theory of communal effort back towards individual enterprise.

What are the conclusions to be drawn from these relatively few years of Communist experiment? It is easy to mock at the failure of the theorist. It is easy to point with scorn at the failure to achieve the ambitious programmes of the planners, and at the continual recurrence of drought and flood and insect pest: it is easy too, to decry the removal of family life from the villages, as must happen to some extent when women work in the fields and on roadmaking or irrigation schemes, and children are cared for in schools and communal nurseries. There are many tales from those who have left their villages and escaped from China telling of the hardships of village life in the communes, and the unhappiness of those who remain there. These tales may well be true, just as it is true that in spite of its boasts the government has failed to remove the threat of flood and drought. But against this must be set the life of the cultivator in pre-Communist China. Floods and droughts and starvation were common then: women worked in the fields in those days, and had little time to care for their children: and although the food in the mess-halls of the communes may be sparse and poor it should be compared, not with the well-filled table of the prosperous peasant, but with the bowl of rice of the pre-Communist debt-ridden share-cropper.

In 15 years China has been passing through the turmoil and suffering that is inevitable when an age-old system tries to modernise itself in the twinkling of an eye. In another 15 years will it have succeeded in producing enough food for its huge and growing population? Will it have added happiness to the lives of the cultivators? Will the suffering it has caused bear fruit of a sort to warrant this suffering? Could such fruit have been produced with less bloodshed and misery? These are hard, perhaps impossible questions to answer: but an answer, albeit tentative, must be given by any who attempt to decide what are the best means of solving the agricultural and agrarian problems of any country.

7

Non-Communist Methods

HITHERTO, with the exception of Western Germany, the happenings that have been described have taken place in countries with governments pledged to the implementation, in one form or another, of Communist doctrines. Before attempting to summarise such evidence as may be adduced from the experiences of these countries it might be of help to see what has happened in one or two areas where non-Communist methods have been tried.

Europe does not offer a good field for study since most countries there have already reached the stage where not only is there no need for further agricultural production, but where agricultural surpluses present the major problem. Two examples have therefore been chosen, one from Africa and one from the Western Hemisphere, to show how agricultural production can be increased, and the general standard of living of the community raised, without resorting to the drastic methods of Communism. Both examples are on a small scale. This is made necessary by the fact that only where there is a totalitarian government is it possible to plan on a nation-wide scale. In countries where government planning and control is not all-embracing, and where scope is allowed for a considerable degree of individual initiative, changes in landownership, or in methods of production and marketing can only be introduced on a relatively small scale. If the results are seen to be good and others wish to share in the benefits, these schemes can be extended: but they are not imposed by government decree upon an entire nation.

The first example is taken from Africa, from the valley of the Nile. The Gezira Plain covers about 5 million acres in the Sudan, between the Blue and White Niles just south of Khartoum. At the beginning of the twentieth century, when the British came to Khartoum, there were a few settled villages close to the river, but in the Plain itself cultivation was on a nomadic basis. The soil was intrinsically rich but rainfall was too uncertain to permit of any fixed and settled cultivation excepting close to the river banks where primitive irrigation could be practised. But in less than half a century a great change had taken place. By 1950 nearly one million acres, or one-fifth of the total area, were under regular cultivation, of which over 200,000 were in cotton, this alone bringing in a total return of 16 million £E's.

The history of this agricultural development, although by no means one of uninterrupted success, is an example of happy co-operation between Government, private capital, and peasant. It started with the grant by the Sudan Government in 1903 first to a private individual and then to a Syndicate (The Sudan Experimental Plantations Syndicate) of 10,000 acres in the Gezira Plain. In return for this concession the Syndicate undertook the job of irrigation with the object of developing cotton cultivation. This relatively small commercial undertaking developed, to a large extent due to Lord Kitchener, then Governor of the Sudan, into a three-sided partnership. The Government of the Sudan provided land: the Syndicate, formed by private shareholders and banking houses, provided the capital for the extensive irrigation works and also undertook the marketing of the cotton that was to be grown: and the Sudanese peasants provided the manpower for the actual cultivation.

The division of the profits was based on age-old custom. This had established that the owner of the land was entitled to one-tenth of the crop, and whoever owned and maintained the water-wheel necessary for irrigation took a further tenth. The owner of the cattle that was grazed upon the land took one-fifth of the crop, the supplier of the cattle fodder took two-thirtieths, and the supplier of seed and implements took four-thirtieths. All these shares added up to a total of 60 per cent of the entire crop, leaving the working tenant 40 per cent. Following this custom it was agreed that the cultivator should, as in the past, retain 40 per cent of the crop while the remaining 60 per cent should be divided between the Sudanese Government and the Syndicate who provided the capital.

Under the original agreement between the Government and the Syndicate the former took 35 per cent and the latter 25 per cent, but this was later modified so that the Government received 40 per cent and the Syndicate 20 per cent. This division referred only to cotton, which was the sole cash crop: the other two crops, being grain which was retained as food for the tenant and his family, and beans used as fodder for the cattle, were the sole property of the tenant himself.

Before the First World War the scheme was in its infancy, and only covered a small area of ground. But in 1920 (significantly, at about the same time as the Russian land reform got under way) the area under cultivation extended to 300,000 acres. This land was already in private ownership but of relatively low value owing to the absence of irrigation. It was an intrinsic part of the scheme that owners would not be deprived of their ownership, and that they would retain all their existing rights of transfer and mortgage. The Government, however, hired all the land within the irrigation area and paid rent for it—other than small acreages which, being necessary for the actual permanent works of irrigation, were bought outright. The period of the lease was for 40 years, but the Government had the right to continue it for a further period if it seemed to be in the public interest to do so. The rent paid by the Government was a fixed one, based on the low unirrigated value. Tenancies of the irrigated land were allocated in the first instance to existing owners, the amount they were granted being limited to that which they and their immediate family could cultivate. The tenant paid no rent or irrigation dues on his land other than the 60 per cent of the cotton crop already referred to: the remaining 40 per cent, as well as all other crops and proceeds from the sale of livestock, were his.

By 1925 the new scheme was well under way. The dam was completed and 300,000 acres were irrigated, on this 100,000 acres of cotton being grown. The whole area was divided into blocks averaging about 15,000 acres and in each block were half a dozen or so villages. Arthur Gaitskell* describes the organisation of such a village: 'Talha was a large village and, on the basis of 30 feddans (acres) gross per tenancy, the people were entitled by right of ownership of some 3,000 feddans to 100 tenancies. They had seen their lands gradually covered by the irrigation grid, the canals laid out and dug by the Irrigation Department, the field-channels under the supervision of the Syndicate's block inspector. They already knew him. They had sought his intervention to get a canal diverted round the graveyard at Heleiwa village and his help to get compensation for Mohammed Dafalla when the excavations ran through his dura (grain) before he had a chance to harvest. . . . Gradually the privately owned land is allotted. The biggest landowners in Talha are the heirs of Sheikh Ahmed El Tereifi, a local aristocracy owning some

* *Gezira*, p. 100, Faber & Faber, 1959.

780 feddans. One hundred and eighty feddans is the next largest unit but large units are rare and less than 30 feddans admits a preferential claim to tenancy. A few large owners may get two tenancies in their own name, but never more, for the rule is that the owner's personal allotment is confined to what they can manage and it is strictly adhered to. The Government's aim was that each tenant should work his own holding. . . . In this first allotment most of the male population got tenancies. Later, as children grow up, absentees return and economic changes bring new employment, the non-tenant population will increase and within twenty years tenancies will form but half the population. . . .'

Cultivation was carried out under the direction of the Syndicate's inspector who was also responsible for the orderly irrigation of the different plots, for the supply of seed, as well as of tools. The inspector was authorised to grant loans, and he also had the power to evict an unsatisfactory tenant, though this in fact was never used. Under this form of paternalistic direction the project prospered, apart from a few years when disease and low cotton prices coincided and caused considerable hardship to tenants, and financial loss to shareholders.

By 1940 the scheme was well established on an economic footing, the method of cultivation had improved, marketing was satisfactory and yields were high by comparison with earlier days. It was then felt that something more was needed than a purely economic undertaking. The social development of the area should now become a matter of high importance. These views were embodied in a declaration of policy agreed between the Government and the Syndicate. This declaration stated:

'The Government's general policy is to train up a class of small farmers, who, when the concession period is ended, can make the best use of the permanent irrigation system established in the Gezira.

The Government's administrative policy is:

(a) The development of an orderly organisation of village communities controlled by headsmen selected by themselves.
(b) The devolution of civic and agricultural control of the farmers to agents of this organisation (i.e. agricultural sheikhs) and the use of village and other councils and of native courts to support and enforce the authority of these agents.
(c) The gradual substitution of Sudanese for all non-British employees and eventually the use of Sudanese agriculturalists in the field in an advisory capacity.

The Government's agricultural policy is:

(a) The production of a class of mixed farmers with a permanent stake in the land which they farm. To this end:
(b) The cultivation of food and fodder crops should be given as much importance as the money crop.
(c) Provision should be made for the agricultural education of native agents and selected farmers.'

During the ensuing years this policy was put into force. In the meantime the Sudan had been freed from all colonial fetters, and had become in no sense subservient to Great Britain. Again to quote Gaitskell (op. cit. p. 216): 'Our basic assumption in this programme was a future picture of a co-operative community of farmers capable of managing their local affairs through their village units, assisted meantime by our organisation whose duty was to make this community one of healthy, intelligent and progressive men and women. For development at the centre, we envisaged the village councils appointing representatives to the block councils and from these, later, a small representative board of tenants for the whole Gezira.

'The idea was that through such a board consultation at first, and much later on control, might pass from the

92

present system to an appointed or elected body of tenants representing and managing the Tenants' Co-operative Society. We looked on this social development programme as something additional to, not competing with, economic efficiency.'

In 1944 the Syndicate, which, it will be remembered, consisted of private shareholders, was informed by the British Government of the day that they would not renew the Syndicate's concession after 1950. This in itself was enough to pave the way for a more rapid move towards self-government and social advance; but this move was helped by the rising profitability of the Syndicate's operations. In the last four years of the partnership between Government, Syndicate and cultivator, that is from 1946 to 1950, the profit per acre had risen from £E13 to £E78, the profit per tenant from £E29 to £E281, and the Government's direct surplus from the scheme from under £E1,000,000 to over £E16,000,000. At the same time the profit to the shareholders in the Syndicate had risen from £E7,500,000 to £E16,000,000.

By 1955 the Sudan Gezira Board, which had taken over from the Syndicate responsibility for managing the scheme, had as its Managing Director a Sudanese and both the British Government and British capital had disappeared from the scene. The agricultural side of the enterprise was still prospering and money accumulated in previous years for social development was beginning to bear fruit. There was an agricultural training school for tenants' sons, there were women welfare workers teaching sewing and cooking, and a health visitor teaching child welfare: there were anti-malarial experiments and a centre for bilharzia research. There were village councils and the Tenants' Representative Body; there was adult education and a local newspaper; and there were many plans for the future—co-operative shops, travelling libraries, an animal breeding centre and many other opportunities for social advance. But the outstanding fact is that in the thirty-five years from 1920 to 1955 the Gezira scheme has, by forming a partnership between Government, private capital, and cultivator, made an enormous contribution to the total wealth of the area, and has ensured that the main beneficiaries in the long run are the cultivators themselves. This has been achieved not only without interference with the traditional liberties of the cultivator but with an actual increase in them; at the same time there has been brought about a greater equality of wealth and a greater opportunity for youth than has ever before been known in the Gezira Plain.

An example of a different kind of agricultural expansion comes from a small island in the Caribbean. St. Lucia is one of the members of the Federation of the West Indies, an island of some 150,000 acres and 100,000 inhabitants. Originally occupied by Spain it was for many years in the possession of France, becoming a British colony at the beginning of the nineteenth century. Its economy was based on sugar production, the plantations being worked by African slave labour. After the abolition of slavery by the British, sugar production declined: for many years the island remained poor, living on small exports not only of sugar, but also of limes and coconuts, helped by the employment offered by the fact that it was one of the main Caribbean coaling stations for the British Navy and merchant shipping: for the harbour of Castries was the best deep-water harbour of the area. With the advent of oil this importance as a coaling station disappeared, and between the two World Wars the island's agricultural production was at a very low level; in fact it depended to a very great extent upon grants from the British government for its essential services.

The Second World War hit St. Lucia severely. It did not suffer from direct enemy action, but it did suffer

rom the inability, through shipping shortages, to export
iny of its normal products. It was, therefore, necessary
when the war came to an end, to rebuild almost from the
beginning. There were no internal capital accumulations
or investment, the few relatively large landowners were
short of resources, and the large mass of peasant-proprietors were able to do little else than produce from
their land enough food for their own immediate needs.

In spite of these handicaps by 1959 the island's gross
exports had risen from the 1945 figure of one million
pounds sterling to just under £2,000,000, while imports
had risen from £360,000 to just over £2,000,000. In place
of 125 miles of main and second class roads in 1948 by
1959 it had nearly double the length—222 miles; it had
618 cars in place of 216 in 1949, and its population in
1959 could afford to import £540,000 worth of foodstuffs
annually instead of £120,000 worth in 1945. In 1945 it
imported practically no artificial fertilisers, while in 1958
the value of fertiliser imports was £75,000.

This new wealth came primarily from bananas, but
also from copra, sugar, and cocoa, and to achieve such
an increase in production both private and governmental
sources were mobilised. The United Kingdom government in the same period gave or lent to St. Lucia nearly
£2,500,000 and thus private capital was in this way
reinforced by State capital. The sugar crop was guaran-
teed, both market and price, under the Commonwealth
Sugar Agreement, and copra was given an assured market
by an agreement entered into by the independent governments of all the British West Indian islands as well as
British Guiana and British Honduras. Cocoa was developed to meet the needs of the market by means of the
issue of free cocoa plants to all growers as well as by
technical assistance and a government-sponsored (though
in part private-enterprise-supported) programme of research into the breeding of varieties with heavier yields

and better quality. But it was bananas which were responsible for the greatest increase in the wealth of the island, and this was achieved by a long-term agreement entered into between the private enterprise buyer and by the growers of the island co-operating together in a banana marketing association.

In these ways all cultivators and landowners whether large or small (and in St. Lucia the peasant-proprietor is numerically in an enormous majority) have not only been encouraged to produce more, but at the same time have been given sufficient confidence in the future so that they have felt it wise to invest a part of their profits in further expansion.

The results are manifold. With higher profits more fertiliser is being used and yields are increasing. Wages are rising and the worker as well as the peasant can afford better dwellings and more amenities as well as more nutritious food: the Government's revenue from taxes has increased so it has become less dependent upon grants from Great Britain, and can devote an increasing amount of money to the provision of roads, schools, and other public services. Piped water supply is being developed, as is main electricity, and although the gap between rich and poor is still very wide it is by degrees being narrowed, without discouraging those with capital from investing it in the island and still providing sufficient incentive to the peasant and the worker to earn more.

Hand in hand with this economic freedom has come political emancipation. St. Lucia now has its own elected Legislative Assembly, with its own elected Ministers. It is a member of the Federation of the West Indies which is on the point of being released from its colonial status, and of becoming an independent member of the British Commonwealth, with complete power to order its own affairs. Such help as has been given from Great Britain as therefore been manifestly given with no political rings attached, and the improvement in the economic fe of St. Lucia has not been bought in exchange for olitical servitude, any more than has the prosperity of ie cotton-growers of the Gezirah. In both these regions has been shown to be possible to achieve in a relatively ort time a marked improvement in the standard of ving of those who cultivate the soil without in any way iterfering either with their political or their economic berty.

8

In Conclusion

THE preceding chapters have in the main dealt with som
of those countries where Communist agricultural polic
has been put to the practical test. They have touched o
some of the earlier history, and have also shown cond
tions immediately prior to the introduction of the Con
munist régime; and they have attempted to show i
general terms, and without undue use of statistics, th
results that have been obtained in recent years. Thi
may be of some slight historic interest: but it may als
be of help in dealing with future problems.

There are many countries today which are still at a
early stage of their economic development, and whicl
are searching for the best means of improving their ecc
nomic as well as their political status. Among these wil
be found many who are not irrevocably committed eithe
to the capitalist (for want of a better word), or to th
Communist system. These countries are free to decid
for themselves what path they wish to pursue, withou
doctrinaire prejudices or vested interests to obscure th
issues.

Briefly the problems that confront such countries ar
the following. In the first place they are faced with th
need to increase total agricultural production. Not onl
do the people living in these countries suffer in genera
from malnutrition, which, at least in the short-term, car
best be met by increasing their own production of food
but they also suffer from straightforward poverty. Thi
means that the wealth that they produce from their owr
resources, whether agricultural or otherwise, is insuf

cient to meet their own internal needs and leave a
surplus available to exchange with the outside world
or those raw materials and finished products, whether
hey be oil or motor cars, cotton or clothing, which are
essential to an increased standard of living: nor is there
sufficient surplus to allow for investment from which
can come greater output.

Secondly, the number of people employed in agriculture, whether expressed as a percentage of the total population or in absolute numbers, must be reduced. Within
wide limits a country's standard of living corresponds
inversely to the percentage of the population engaged in
agriculture. A community in which the whole population
has to spend all its time producing food for its own use
must be a poor community because no time or labour is
available for any of those other things which add to the
richness of life. A community which can meet its entire
food requirements by employing only 10 per cent of its
working population in food production has a high standard of living because 90 per cent of its working population can devote their efforts to the production of clothing,
housing, education, medical health, and non-essentials
such as motor cars, radios, and works of art—as well as to
the enjoyment of leisure. It must therefore be the aim of
any country desirous of improving its standard of living
to release some of those who are today engaged in food
production so as to enable them to devote their efforts
to other activities.

The third essential, without which neither of the first
two can be effectively achieved, is to encourage capital
investment in food production. Without capital investment the land must be tilled by manual labour helped
only by primitive implements such as mattocks and
spades. The crop must grow as best it can, relying only
on such innate fertility as there is in the soil, unassisted
by manufactured fertilisers. The finished product must

be transported on the back or the head over mountai
paths and through forest tracks to the centre of consum
tion. If capital is available more land will be cleare
because there will be machinery available to do th
clearing. That which is already tilled can be cultivate
by machines which, with only one operator, can perfor
the work of twenty or even a hundred men: worn-ou
and frequently diseased seed can be replaced by scie
tifically-bred healthy stock, and encouraged to yield
the utmost of its capacity with the help of artificial fert
lisers and irrigation, and protected against disease an
insect pests by suitable chemicals: and when these heavi
crops which have been grown with less labour are final
harvested they can then, given sufficient capital,
loaded on to lorries and transported along hard roac
not only to the local towns for consumption, but to mo
distant harbours for export to industrial countries whic
in exchange will send back the produce of their factorie

Fourthly, neither the co-operation nor the happines
of those concerned must be forgotten. The primar
object of the operation is the betterment of the whol
country, and the country consists of the individuals wh
live in it. In all but the most highly developed countri
it is the cultivators who make up the great majority
the population: so, unless the condition of the cultivato
themselves is improved, the operation, however successf
in theory, will have failed in its object. Force and con
pulsion may be justified if they are used to prevent
minority from impeding the just desires of the majorit
they may even be justified if they are used to force
majority to adopt a policy which is to their long-ter
benefit but which they oppose through ignorance or a
intrinsic dislike of change. But they cannot be justifie
nor do the policies themselves have any great chance
success, if year after year the cultivator continues in hi

sistance and refuses to accept the benefits which the
new system should bring him.

It is idle to suppose that any of these objectives, let
alone all of them, can be achieved by running counter to
the prevailing trend of political thought in the world.
One hundred years ago, at the time of the great industrial expansion in Western Europe, agricultural expansion also developed at a great pace, and at the same time
capital poured into it, just as it did into industry. This
flow of capital was achieved only because the private
investors saw opportunities to double or quadruple their
capital. With this rosy prospect in view they were prepared to take risks, and although some of them lost their
all many made vast fortunes and the total wealth of
their country grew. But those who were unable to save
sufficient from their daily requirements (and there were a
thousand of these for every one who was able to save
sufficient to invest) did not share in the increased wealth,
and the gap between the rich and the poor magnified.

This is something which no modern country intent on
increasing its total wealth can tolerate. So means must be
worked out by which a sufficiently attractive return is
offered to the investor, whether he be a private individual, a corporation, or a foreign government, but at
the same time the fresh wealth that is produced is shared
equitably throughout the whole of the country.

From the experiences outlined in earlier chapters, how
far does Communism offer the answer to these complex
problems? To take the last question first, it must be true
that the gross inequalities of wealth which existed before
Communism in such countries as Russia, Hungary, Yugoslavia, or Eastern Germany, have now to a great extent
disappeared. True, there are still the rich and the poor;
there are still a few who can afford motor cars, while
tens of thousands plod to their work through the country
mud on their feet, or queue in the city streets for public

101

transport to take them to their offices or their factories a few have summer villas in the country in addition t comfortable apartments in town, while tens of thousand of families are crowded together six people to a room true there are some who can afford to eat at expensive restaurants and go to night-clubs and theatres while ten of thousands have to be content with black bread an cabbage soup for their nourishment, and do not even have a neighbour's radio to listen to in the evening: an it is also true that the children of those who are i influential positions receive a better education and ge a better start in life than do the children of the factor worker or the farm worker. But for all that no grea fortunes have been made out of the exploitation of th country's resources, and the vast differences that existe in the last century between the rich and poor have with out doubt been narrowed.

On this score, therefore, Communism can claim considerable success—though if a comparison is to be made between the Communist and the non-Communist world it must be remembered that the gap between the rich and poor, between privileged and under-privileged even in the non-Communist world has shrunk remark ably in the last fifty years also.

How have the Communist countries fared when i comes to investment? Here they have one great advan tage and one great disadvantage. The disadvantage i that they cannot attract capital from non-Communist countries: these are understandably chary of investing money, whether governmental or private, in areas where the Communist doctrine prevails—though there are ex ceptions, such as Yugoslavia, which has in fact received substantial credits from non-Communist sources. The advantage is that the entire national investment pro gramme is planned by the government, and it is for them to decide how much of the country's resources are to b lowed for current personal expenditure, how much on current government expenditure, such as defence; and how much should be reinvested. Of this latter sum they must also decide how much is to be allocated to agriculture, and how much to industry.

It is impossible to make a direct comparison here with non-Communist countries: but it must be remembered that even in these latter, governments undertake, both nationally and internationally, the investment of capital in long-term agricultural projects; and are able, in a general and often indirect way, to exercise some control over the manner in which investments are made, encouraging some types and discouraging others by such means as differential taxation or interest rates. The Tennessee Valley Authority, harnessing the waters of the Tennessee River to control erosion and flood, irrigate, produce cheap electric power for fertiliser production and other factories, was brought into being by the direct action of the United States government, and served as a model for the Volta Valley scheme in West Africa, the Kariba Dam in Southern Rhodesia, and many smaller projects. The Colombo Plan makes money available on an international basis for large-scale, long-term investment in countries which have insufficient resources of their own. And there are countless smaller investments of a similar nature throughout the world, in Italy and Australia, in Morocco and India, just as there are in Russia and Yugoslavia, in China and in Hungary.

But in spite of long and impressive lists of investment in agriculture no country has enough money to proceed with much-needed schemes as fast as it would like: and in Communist countries, as in others, where the need for investment is greatest, so also is the shortage of capital most acute. These poorer countries have no alternative but to rely on the generosity of their richer Communist neighbours, and even Russia, the richest of them all, has

so much need for internal investment that it is unlike
that she will invest money outside her own borders unle
she can see in such an investment strong advantage
economic, military or political, for herself.

Furthermore, experience has shown that in general
is the non-rural type of investment which has receive
the highest priority. Construction of factories and dwe
ing houses for factory workers has taken priority ov
land reclamation, irrigation, and rural housing: ar
where agricultural investment has taken place it h
usually been on a grandiose scale designed for the lon
term State enterprise, rather than being of the sort whic
will bring benefit to the existing cultivator and a
immediate increase in production.

Here too, then, no clear-cut answer can be given. E
perience shows that both in Communist and non-Cor
munist countries investment has been directed in
agriculture in varying degrees, and with varying succes
but there is no evidence to support the contention th
in the matter of capital investment either system shov
a marked superiority over the other.

When we turn to the shift in working population awa
from agriculture and into industry the picture vari
widely from country to country: and here statistics ma
be of some value. Pre-war Russia had an agricultur
population of 97 million, or just over 50 per cent, whic
after the war dropped to about 45 per cent. In Yug
slavia in 1931, 76 per cent of the population were e
gaged in agriculture: by 1951 this had fallen to 73 p
cent, and by 1960 was about 50 per cent. But even the
improved figures are still a long way from those
the United States of America, Western Germany and th
United Kingdom. In the United States, for instanc
the agricultural population was in 1955 13 per cent
the total compared with 22 per cent in 1940: in Wester
Germany it was in 1950 15 per cent compared wit

8 per cent in 1939: and in the United Kingdom it is
ow less than 5 per cent, compared with the 1931 figure
f 6 per cent. Whether the progress would have been
reater without Communism is anybody's guess. All that
an be said is that some progress has been made but there
 still a long way to go: while the country that has made
ie greatest progress is Yugoslavia, where the implemen-
ttion of orthodox Communist doctrines has, as has been
iown in a previous chapter, been largely tempered by
ractical realities.

Finally, what about production and the conditions
nd happiness of the cultivator? Earlier chapters have
ttempted to give evidence on both these matters which
ill enable the reader to draw his own conclusions. But
nce again the danger of undue reliance on statistics
iust be emphasised. Especially in the matter of yields,
 any farmer knows, even with the same management
nd identical techniques the harvest can vary 100 per
:nt from year to year depending solely upon weather.
ny valid statistical analysis must cover a period of at
:ast ten years, and, apart from Russia, Communism has
ot been tried for long enough to enable a comparison
etween two ten-year periods to be made. Furthermore,
i any country which was devastated by the Second
Vorld War (as were most of the new Communist coun-
ies) production was at such a low level in 1945 that a
gnificant increase should have taken place no matter
hat political system had been in force.

To summarise very briefly it is clear that the intro-
uction of Communism into the countryside, in no
iatter what country, leads, in the early stages, to resist-
nce, unhappiness, and a fall in production. Where, as
i Yugoslavia, the government adapts its policies so as
) co-operate with the peasant, production can rise
uickly and both producer and consumer, cultivator
nd town-dweller, share in the increased prosperity.

Where, as in the Soviet Union, no lasting compromise effected, but compulsion is used to force the peasar into the Communist way of life, many years must elap before production begins once more to resume its norm advance: while a whole new generation of peasants, agricultural workers, as they have now become, mu arise before there is any chance of a willing acceptan of the new order and only a minority are left who regr the passing of 'the good old days'.

What, then, should be the conclusions arrived at the planners and political thinkers in countries whic still have far to go along the path of political econom development, when they turn their minds to agricu tural and agrarian problems? For all these countri must decide their own future. They must not be dictate to by others nor must the speed or manner of the advance be dependent upon the political doctrines foreign governments. They may be fortunate enough receive help, either material or in the form of advic from elsewhere, but the decision as to what form society or what form of government they want to see their own country must be entirely theirs. These d cisions will depend to a large extent on the history ar the background of the country itself; what is suitable f Central Africa may well be entirely unsuited to Sout east Asia, and what succeeds in the Caribbean may fa in the Middle East. Note must be taken of the succe or failures of rival methods, and their significan assessed, but they must not be accepted without questio

One thing that stands out uncontrovertibly is that r agricultural reform, no matter how attractive it may in theory, can have any chance of success unless it carried through with the full co-operation and goodwi of the cultivator himself. Bearing this in mind, and pr vided they are not already committed to one politic

octrine or another, those who are anxious to work out
ays and means of helping their own country and the
eople living in it must surely say something of this sort.
'rivate enterprise on its own will not bring about the
xpansion of agricultural production that we wish for,
the speed that we need. Nor is it likely, in any case, to
ucceed without bringing about, at the same time, gross
equalities in wealth of the sort that we cannot tolerate.
'On the other hand unadulterated Communism also
ucceeds only after many years, and after imposing suf-
ring on many who we wish to help rather than hurt. So
e shall use the resources of the State to plan the out-
nes of our agricultural production, and to undertake
e great works of capital investment which are beyond
e powers of individual farmers. We shall also legislate
prevent power being exercised by those with no claim
it other than that they own land, and to ensure that
ose who actually cultivate the soil and produce the
ops obtain a fair reward for their labours. At the same
me the State will, when necessary, regulate prices to
event the consumer being exploited by producer or
iddle-men, and to prevent also the exploitation of the
oducer by the buyer. We shall also use the resources
the State to provide credit for individual farmers to
able them to make use of modern techniques, whether
mechanisation, fertilisers, breeding stock or pedigree
eds: and we shall undertake both research and educa-
on to ensure that the results of this research will be
anslated with the least possible delay into action in the
lds themselves. In this way we can expect to achieve
rapid increase in agricultural production, a just distri-
ition of the ensuing wealth, and contentment among
oth producer and consumer.'
Those who follow this line of reasoning will succeed
building up the agriculture, and therefore the wealth,
their country and at the same time will achieve the

happiness of their people. Those who are the blind adherents of dogma, of no matter what political shade, will not only fail in their economic objectives, but will be responsible for widespread misery and poverty for many years ahead among those very people whom they set out to help.